Gem Trails of Colorado

by
James R. Mitchell

Gem Guides Book Co.
315 Cloverleaf Drive, Suite F
Baldwin Park, CA 91706

Library of Congress Catalog Card Number: 96-80263
ISBN 0-935182-91-8

Maps: Jean Hammond
Cover: Mark Webber

NOTE:
    Due to the possibility of personal error, typographical error, misinterpretation of information, and the many changes due to man or nature, *Gem Trails of Colorado*, its publisher and all other persons directly or indirectly associated with this publication assume no responsibility for accidents, injury or any losses by individuals or groups using this publication.
    In rough terrain and hazardous areas all persons are advised to be aware of possible changes due to man or nature that occur along the gem trails.

TABLE OF CONTENTS

MAP LEGEND

▬▬▬▬▬	Interstate Highway
▬▬▬▬	U.S. Highway
▬▬▬	State Highway
═══	Divided Highway
────	Local Road
■-■-■-■	Gravel Graded Road
═══	Graded Dirt Road
= = = = = =	Unimproved Dirt Road
– – – – – –	Trail
(25)	Interstate Highway
(85)	U.S. Highway
(67)	State Highway
[40]	Forest or County Road
✕	Mine
≡	Cattle Guard
⊠	Gate
⚠	Campground

KEY TO SITES ON MAP

REGION I

Site No.

(1) Yampa River
(2) Elk Springs
(3) Douglas Pass
(4) Grand Junction
(5) Opal Hill
(6) Parachute
(7) Kremmling
(8) Parshall
(9) Owl Canyon
(10) Green Mountain Reservoir
(11) Marble
(12) Alma
(13) Leadville Mines

REGION II

(14) Raymer
(15) Stoneham
(16) Perry Park
(17) Fern Creek
(18) Devil's Head
(19) Pine Creek
(20) Golden
(21) Golden Gate
(22) Leyden
(23) Nederland

REGION III

(24) Hartsel
(25) Wilkerson Pass West
(26) Wilkerson Pass East
(27) Lake George
(28) Round Mountain
(29) Tarryall
(30) Topaz Mountain Gem Mine
(31) Florissant Crystals
(32) Florissant Fossils
(33) Calhan Badlands
(34) St. Peter's Dome
(35) Pueblo

Site No.

(36) Penrose
(37) Canon City
(38) Royal Gorge Area
(39) Border Feldspar Mine
(40) Texas Creek
(41) La Veta Pass
(42) Trinidad

REGION IV

(43) Gateway
(44) Whitewater
(45) Piñon Mesa
(46) Trout Creek
(47) Nathrop
(48) Mt. Antero
(49) Calumet Mine
(50) Salida
(51) Homestake
(52) Parlin
(53) Saguache
(54) La Garita
(55) Cochetopa Hills
(56) Twin Peaks
(57) Wolf Creek Pass
(58) Creede Mines
(59) Silverton Mines
(60) Ouray Mines

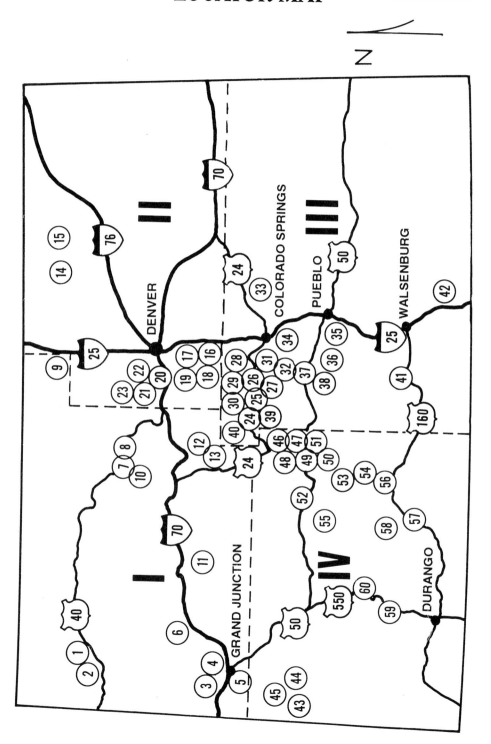

INTRODUCTION

The primary purpose of this field guide is to provide information to those with an interest in collecting gems, minerals, and fossils as a hobby. Do not assume, however, that the data presented will enable the casual rock hunter to gather great quantities of valuable material by just driving along major highways. For the best hunting, one is usually required to travel on side roads, hike along creek beds, or trek to other such remote regions.

The directions given are presented as accurately and detailed as possible. Keep in mind that mileage can vary according to odometer accuracy and slippage of tires on dirt roads. Each place was checked shortly before publication to verify that something worthwhile could be found. It is not guaranteed, however, that a specific spot will amply supply all collectors. If directions are followed, though, you should not go home empty-handed.

Some of the spots are privately owned and either a fee is charged and/or collecting is restricted. The author attempted to mention such information in the text, but status changes rapidly, especially on private land. For that reason, please DO NOT ASSUME THAT THIS GUIDE GIVES PERMISSION TO COLLECT! If you have suspicions that a particular site is no longer open, be sure to ascertain the situation before trespassing. If nothing can be determined locally, land ownership information is available at the County Recorder's office.

There are millions of acres of land in public domain throughout the United States where rockhounds can collect at will, and lots of such territory is in Colorado. Due to Colorado's prominent mining history, however, most of the best mineral specimens are associated with that industry, frequently restricting access. Additionally, other sites are on private ranch land or on leased regions of national forests, both requiring permission from the owners or leaseholders before collecting. Be certain to respect those rights at all times. Usually, Colorado ranchers and landowners are most cordial and allow people onto their land, if they are given the courtesy of being asked ahead of time. Claim holders, however, may be more hesitant due to insurance restrictions associated with shafts, tunnels and collapsing buildings on their property.

If you do collect on dumps of abandoned mines, DO NOT, under any circumstances, enter shafts, and always be cautious when exploring the surrounding regions. There are often hidden tunnels, rotted ground and pits, as well as rusty nails, broken glass and discarded chemicals; all of which create a potential hazard.

Most areas discussed on the following pages are easy to get to, but road conditions can change. Severe weather may make good roads very rough, and very rough roads impassable, even with four-wheel drive. Do not attempt traveling where your vehicle was not designed to go.

In addition, these sites are situated in a variety of different landscapes, ranging from flatlands to steep and precarious mountains. Because of these differences, avoid trips to the hot flatlands during the sweltering summer months, or to the mountains during the frigid winter when roads are traditionally closed due to heavy snows. Be also advised, even during the summer months, snowstorms and severe electrical storms can occur, especially at the higher elevations. If the weather appears threatening, use good judgment and do not get caught without being adequately prepared. The best policy is, if in doubt, retreat and return another day.

When venturing into some of the more remote areas, it is a good idea to take extra drinking water, foul weather clothing, and possibly even some food, just in case you get delayed or stuck. If you take some time to plan your trip properly and make sure your vehicle is in good working order, the gem fields listed on the following pages will provide you and your family with outstanding minerals, spectacular scenery, fascinating history, and many memorable experiences.

James R. Mitchell

These two locations provide a good sampling of Colorado's colorful agate and jasper. To get to the first, labeled Site A on the accompanying map, proceed seven miles east from Elk Springs along Highway 40 and then go north on the road to Dinosaur National Monument. Drive four more miles and then turn right another one-half mile. At that point, you will find yourself near the banks of the Yampa River where it veers east cutting a canyon through the mountains. This entire region, in virtually any direction for quite a distance, is noted for its fine red, brown and banded agate and jasper.

Be sure to allow enough time to properly explore Site A, since it is extensive and the more easily accessible regions have been somewhat picked over. Be careful, however, if you choose to drive onto any of the side roads, since the terrain is sandy in places. Do not take your vehicle in areas it is not designed to go. Parking and hiking is generally the safest method of exploring if you don't have a rugged four-wheel drive unit. The western slopes of the mountains south of where the Yampa River turns east seem to be the most productive, but going north is certainly not out of the question. Carefully inspect areas of erosion for freshly exposed material. The bright colors of the agate and jasper make it fairly easy to spot, due to the contrast against the lighter colored soil.

If you have a rugged vehicle, continue to Site B. To get there, return to the main road and proceed another one and seven-tenths miles to County Road 25. Go right and drive six and eight-tenths miles to County Road 10 where you must bear left, cross the bridge spanning the Little Snake River, and then take any of the roads or tracks heading south toward the mountains. Be advised that from this point on there is lots of loose sand. If you choose to drive farther, be certain your vehicle is capable of making the trip, since this is a desolate place to get stuck! If unsure, material can be found on either side of County Road 10, continuously, for at least one mile west from the Little Snake River bridge. It is strongly recommended that you restrict the search to that region.

If you do have a rugged four-wheel drive unit, head to the north and eastern slopes of the mountains south of County Road 10, as illustrated on the accompanying map. There are some ruts and an old road leading through the area, but all are periodically washed out, making the journey most challenging. The eastern foothills, between the mountains and the Little Snake River, tend to be the most productive portion of Site B. As mentioned earlier, however, fine material can also be gathered in more accessible regions.

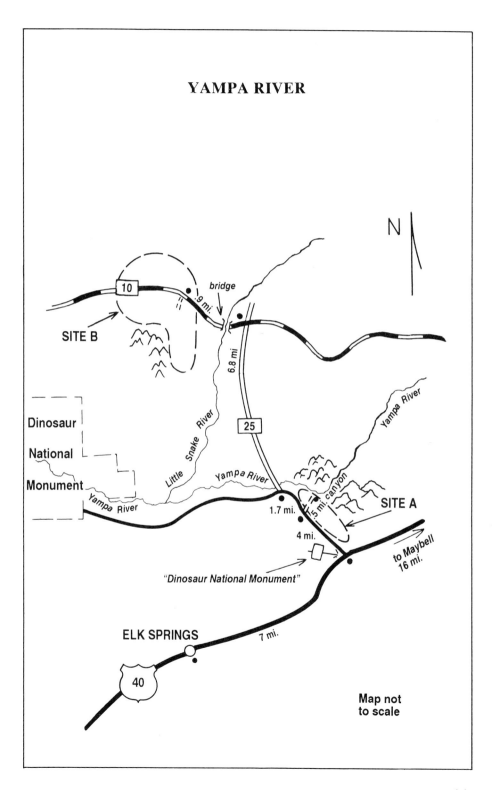

YAMPA RIVER

N

SITE B

10

bridge

.9 mi.

6.8 mi

Dinosaur

National

Monument

Little Snake River

Yampa River

Yampa River

25

Yampa River

1.7 mi.

.5 mi. canyon

SITE A

4 mi.

"Dinosaur National Monument"

to Maybell 16 mi.

ELK SPRINGS

7 mi.

40

Map not
to scale

11

The three locations described here provide an opportunity to gather lots of agate and jasper in a wide variety of colors and patterns. They are situated in a somewhat remote part of the state, however, thereby making it essential to be properly prepared and equipped. Use good judgment, do not drive into regions your vehicle was not intended to traverse, and be willing to allow enough time to adequately explore each of the sites.

To get to the first, Site A, take County Road 14 four and one-half miles north out of Elk Springs. At that point, turn right and follow the rough tracks leading up and into the shallow ravine. Immediately after turning, colorful agate and jasper can be spotted on the road as well as in exposed regions of the surrounding terrain.

Since there is lots of brush and foliage covering the landscape, spend most of your time inspecting places where the ground is not as densely covered, such as in areas of erosion. There is jasper in shades of red, orange buckskin, and yellow, in a variety of color combinations and patterns. In addition, an occasional chunk of agate, some containing interesting inclusions, will be discovered.

Drive as far as you can, stopping and hiking as you proceed, until you have had sufficient opportunity to adequately sample the site. The ruts go for at least one-half mile, but they are so washed out in places that most vehicles will have difficulty getting more than a few tenths of a mile.

Sites B and C can be reached by continuing on County Road 14, but that trip is only for those with a good rugged vehicle and a desire to explore more of the back country. The most efficient way to get there is to return to Highway 40, go west ten and one-half miles to County Road 16, and then proceed northwest fourteen miles to where County Road 14 intersects. From there, and continuing at least one mile north along both sides of County Road 14, collectors can gather bright yellow jasper and nice agate. Some of the specimens contain very interesting patterns and inclusions. Search Site B as you did Site A. Stopping from time to time to sample more than one section of the extensive collecting locale.

Site C is similar to the other two and is accessed by continuing northwest on County Road 16 another three miles, then turning north nine-tenths of a mile, and, finally, either hiking or driving a few hundred yards to the west. From the main road and throughout the terrain to the west, the ground is scattered with additional colorful jasper and agate.

If you have time, be sure to visit nearby Dinosaur National Monument. The Visitors Center is located in the town of Dinosaur, eight miles west of Blue Mountain on Highway 40.

ELK SPRINGS

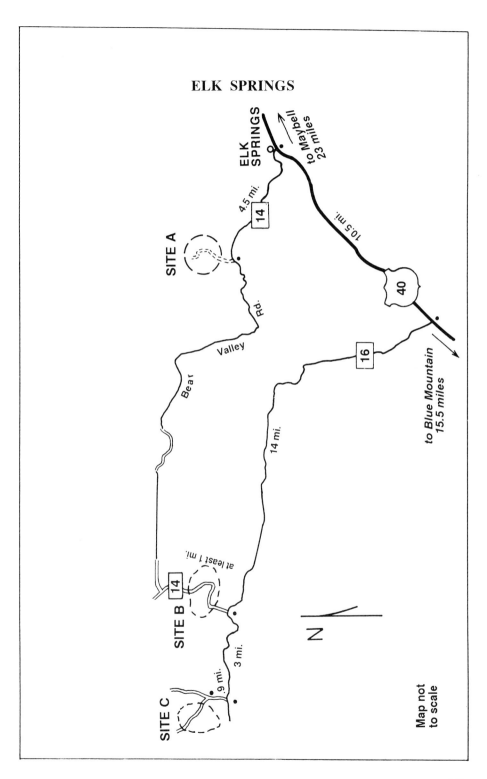

The three sites described here provide a good sampling of one of Colorado's most popular fossil collecting regions. To get the first, Site A, go west from Grand Junction on Interstate 70 to Fruita. Then travel an additional four miles to Highway 139 and Exit 15. Travel north twenty and one-half miles to where a rough dirt road can be seen heading off to the west toward the colorfully banded cliffs a short distance off the pavement. If your vehicle is not capable of driving to the cliffs, simply park well off the highway and hike.

Nice and sometimes colorful leaf fossils can be found by splitting this sedimentary material along bedding planes. For safety reasons, confine the search to boulders and rubble at the base of the cliffs and don't be tempted to do any climbing. Plenty of specimens can be found down below. Just have patience and a willingness to do some hammer and chisel work.

To get to Site B, the most renown of the region's collecting areas, continue north on Highway 139 another twelve and four-tenths miles to where, on the left, the road cuts through a region of oil-rich shale. Another two-tenths of a mile along the way, also on the left, is a deposit of limestone which contains intriguing oolites and tiny fossilized ostracods. These, however, are simply additional intermediate stops on the way to Site B. Proceed another two-tenths of a mile to Douglas Pass Summit, go right, and travel toward the FAA radar dome.

Proceed five and six-tenths miles, bearing left at the forks, to the parking area at the radar dome. Along the way you will pass by some rich oil shale, some of which can be cut and polished to produce very interesting pieces. Search for insect and plant fossils around the parking area as well as up the hill next to the radar station and in regions immediately below. Do not, however, enter the fenced regions. It should be noted that this location is about 9,000 feet above sea level. Take your time and do not overexert. In addition, do not collect during lightning storms, since this is a prime lightning strike area.

The best way to find the fossils is to split suspicious chunks of the Green River shale along layering planes. Hopefully, the plane you expose will contain fossils. If not, keep trying. Do not dig in the radar dome parking area. There is plenty of fossil-bearing rock elsewhere. Over three hundred different species of insects have been discovered from this location and the variety of leaves is equally impressive.

Site C is reached by continuing north on Highway 139 thirteen miles from the radar dome turnoff, as shown on the map. At that point, on the left, are more colorfully banded cliffs, similar to those at Site A, where more leaf fossils can be found. Collect as you did at Site A.

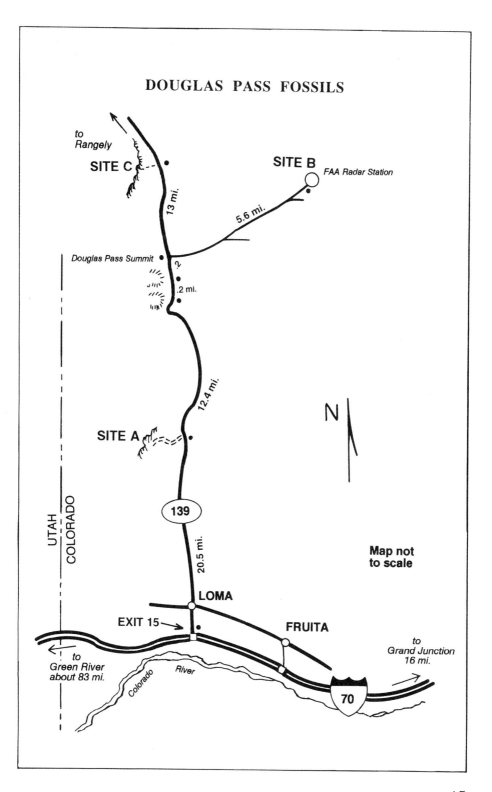

DOUGLAS PASS FOSSILS

to
Rangely

SITE C

SITE B

FAA Radar Station

13 mi.

5.6 mi.

Douglas Pass Summit

.?

.2 mi.

12.4 mi.

N

SITE A

Map not
to scale

139

20.5 mi.

UTAH

COLORADO

LOMA

EXIT 15

FRUITA

to
Grand Junction
16 mi.

to
Green River
about 83 mi.

Colorado   River

70

This location offers collectors barite, selenite and calcite crystals. The water-clear selenite and barite are found on a matrix of yellow, white, or orange rhombohedral calcite, encased within brown, spherical nodules which litter the foothills of Book Cliffs, north of Grand Junction.

To get to one of the most accessible portions of this collecting site, from Grand Junction, go north on 25 Road. About two and one-half miles from where 25 Road crosses Interstate 70, you will make a sharp right and, shortly thereafter, a sharp left. After crossing a canal bridge where the pavement ends, continue north another two and eight-tenths miles to where there is a fork, just past the power lines. Go left, and stay left at the next fork, another three-tenths of a mile. At that point, bear right about one and seven-tenths miles into the mounds and foothills, as illustrated on the map.

There doesn't seem to be any place that is particularly better than another. The hills, stretching for many miles in any direction, offer great possibilities for procuring the barite-filled nodules. Even though the area immediately surrounding the main road is highly picked over, you will be able to spot numerous fragments and pieces, which will enable you to get a much better idea of exactly what to look for. You can also try any of the other countless roads leading alongside Book Cliffs or even do some hiking. If you do hike, however, be sure not to lose your bearings.

The nodules vary in diameter from a few inches to some measuring many feet across, with the average being about one foot. When you find a whole one, carefully split it with a gad or chisel, trying to be as gentle as possible, in an effort not to damage the fragile crystals. The interiors generally contain clear barite and selenite, some of which is facet grade. There is also lots of nice rhombohedral calcite which can be used for specimens in a mineral collection, especially if transparent.

Wash the barite only in room temperature water, since hot or very cold water will cause it to crack. Also be advised that these roads should not be driven on when wet, due to their high clay content.

Parked at the site

GRAND JUNCTION MINERALS

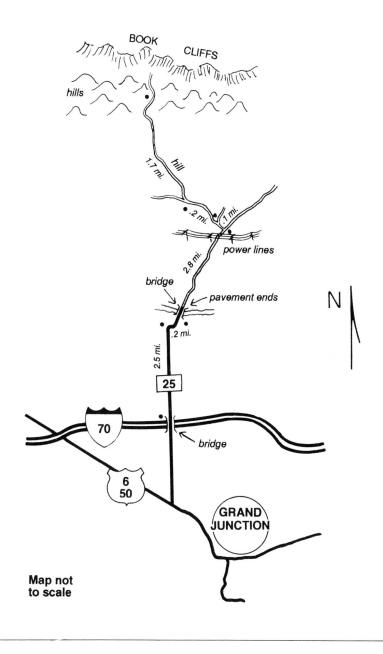

Nice specimens of common opal and opalized wood can be picked up near Opal Hill, only a short drive west of Grand Junction. To get there, take Interstate 70 west approximately twelve miles to the Fruita turnoff. Proceed south one mile, cross the Colorado River, and continue two-tenths of a mile farther. At that point, go right onto King's View Road and drive another seven-tenths of a mile. Or turn left onto the dirt road leading toward Horsethief Canyon. Go only one-tenth of a mile and bear right at the fork. There are some old foundations which help to identify this turn, but they are partially obscured by brush. From there, head toward the ridge, straight ahead, about three-tenths of a mile farther.

All along this ridge, continuing nearly to the river, and in the lowlands below it, one can pick up the beautiful common opal, jasper, selenite, and wood. The opal found here is of a solid, waxy nature, but still quite desirable. Many beautiful stones have been cut from this material. The opal can sometimes be found in vivid shades of orange, red, brown, yellow, blue and even green, with most, though, tending to be brilliant white. Occasionally, a lucky rockhound might stumble upon some prized banded material or specimens filled with moss-like inclusions, which are particularly desirable for cutting and polishing. Generally, the opal is solid and takes a fine polish.

The wood is also desirable, often displaying its original structure in incredible detail. In some, the rings are in contrasting colors and can be used to make very nice display pieces. Most of the wood tends to be in the lower areas and foothills, but occasional chunks can be found in higher regions.

It is suggested that you first explore the lower areas for indications as to what has washed down from the ridge. If you do this before climbing, you may be able to get a better indication of exactly where the better concentrations will be. Take care when climbing onto the ridge as much of the rock is unstable. If you locate a promising opal seam, be sure to wear goggles before trying to remove it from its place on the mountainside. Opal splinters easily when struck with a hammer, and can cause severe damage to the eyes.

View of the collecting area

OPAL HILL

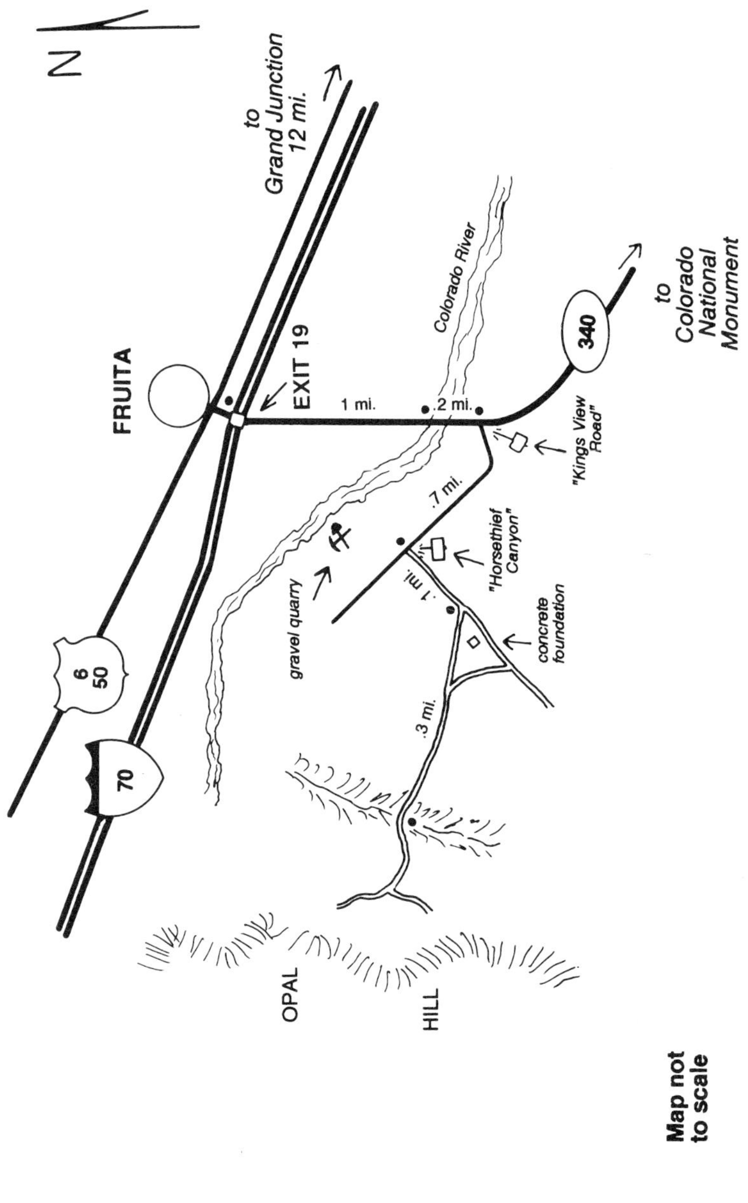

N

to Grand Junction 12 mi.

to Colorado National Monument

Colorado River

FRUITA

EXIT 19

340

"Kings View Road"

1 mi.

.2 mi.

.7 mi.

"Horsethief Canyon"

concrete foundation

gravel quarry

.1 mi.

.3 mi.

6
50

70

OPAL HILL

Map not to scale

Oil shale probably doesn't sound too appealing as a mineral specimen or as something that can be cut and polished to produce beautiful objects of art. The material from the Book Cliff region, east of Grand Junction, however might dispel some of that misgiving. If nothing more, it is interesting to visit this historical site, a location where untold quantities of fossil fuel is trapped within the thin layers of shale.

The oil shale from the regions surrounding the small town of Parachute provides some very nice specimens that take a good polish. In fact, the white, blue, gold, brown and black bandings, in some cases, appear similar to picture stone or a fine banded marble.

Collecting can be done just about anywhere near the Book Cliffs between De Beque and Rifle. Some of the most accessible and top quality material can be obtained by heading north from Parachute on Road 215, into the hills. Be advised, when in this area, that the oil companies do hold leases on most of the oil shale, and collecting is not allowed without prior permission. That shouldn't deter you, though, since there seems to be plenty available in washes and ravines throughout the area, especially along Road 215, and along the banks paralleling Parachute Creek. Road 215 goes about eight miles into a canyon of oil shale and specimens can be gathered just about everywhere.

The color and patterning varies considerably from location to location, so be sure to allow enough time to adequately explore the region, accepting only the least porous and most interesting material you can find. The quantity is so overwhelming that it is easy to gather too much, too early. Sample the region, then you will have a feel for what is good and what is not.

If you plan to cut and polish the oil shale, do so on a slow speed polisher to minimize heat buildup. The hotter temperatures will cause the oil to gum up and damage the exterior. The Book Cliffs oil shale is best used to produce large items such as bookends and clock faces, or to display, as is, in a mineral collection. This material is fascinating, and showing a chunk in your collection will surely initiate a conversation.

Oil shale

PARACHUTE OIL SHALE

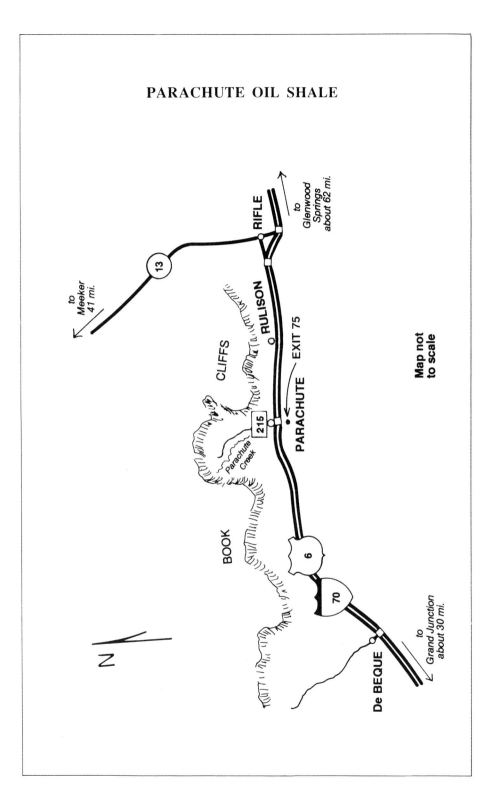

Map not to scale

21

This site offers an opportunity to gather colorful agate and jasper, as well as specimens of petrified wood. To get to the center of the primary collecting area, start in Kremmling, situated about fifty miles southeast of Steamboat Springs, on Highway 40. From town, go east five miles, as shown on the accompanying map, to County Road 2. Turn north and, as you approach milepost 3, there will be some heavily eroded badland-like hills adjacent to the road, on the east. It is within those interesting hills, extending at least another two miles north, that collectors can find the cutting materials.

The best mode for exploring this area is to randomly pull off County Road 2 between mileposts 3 and 5 and indiscriminately hike through the hills. The jasper is easy to spot, since the bright hues of yellow, orange, tan and red stand out against the light colored soil. The agate is just about as easy to spot, but the colors tend to be less vivid. Some is banded and/or filled with interesting inclusions, and the base color tends to be grayish-blue. There is also black agate scattered about, but it is rather plain and uninteresting.

The petrified wood is especially nice, often exhibiting its original wood structure. It tends to be dark, almost black, and some specimens are solid enough to be cut and polished to produce fascinating results. Other pieces, if showing the wood structure especially well, are best simply cleaned and possibly trimmed, but left, as is, for display.

Be sure to stop more than once along the two-mile stretch of County Road 2 comprising the primary collecting area. It is interesting how certain colors and qualities can be found in some places and not in others. There are additional badlands-like mounds farther north, but not as close to the road. If you have the time, they might provide additional material in better quantities, due to the more difficult access. That probably won't be necessary, though, since you should be very satisfied with what can be found in the primary area.

Parked near the hills at the site

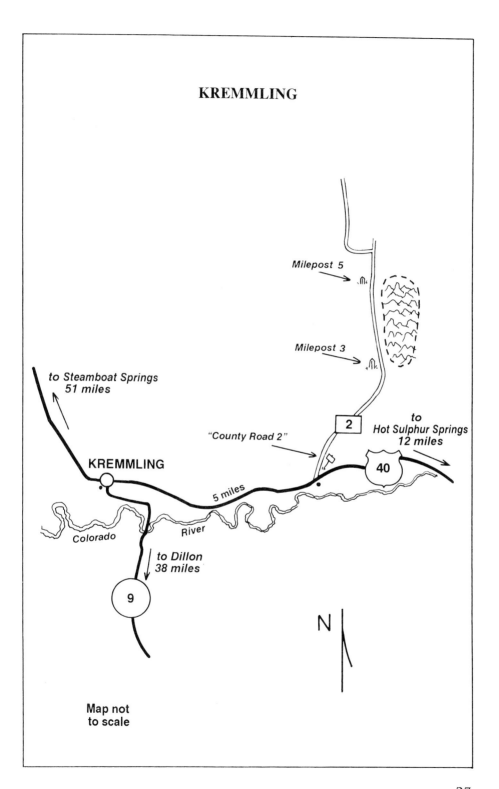

KREMMLING

Milepost 5

Milepost 3

to Steamboat Springs
51 miles

"County Road 2"

2

to
Hot Sulphur Springs
12 miles

KREMMLING

40

5 miles

Colorado   River

to Dillon
38 miles

9

N

Map not
to scale

The Colorado River, near the small town of Parshall, has long been known as a prime supplier of extremely colorful agate and jasper. There is one problem, however. Most of the land on either side of the Colorado River is private, thereby denying easy access to the agate and jasper rich gravels. In addition, Williams Fork, a stream leading from the Colorado River to the Williams Fork Reservoir, is especially renown for its highly productive gravels, but, again, gaining access is difficult.

To get to the Colorado River, itself, use any of the well-marked fishing access roads leading south from Highway 40. Once at the river, examine the gravel and rock on the easily accessible banks and sandbars, but do not venture into the water unless you are certain it is safe to do so. At times the Colorado River is a raging torrent and extremely dangerous, while at other periods, checking out a promising sandbar might be safe.

If you can't find much worthwhile at your first stop, continue along Highway 40 to the next fishing access road and try again. If you want to attempt gaining access to the river from private property, the easiest place to try your luck is in Parshall. Take Parshall Road from Highway 40. After passing through town, an intersection will be encountered and a bridge crosses the river just to the south. Ask at any of the houses or businesses in that area for permission to gather agates. The people here are friendly if you give them the courtesy of explaining your intentions and seeking permission beforehand. That is no guarantee, though.

Another good location is all along the Williams Fork leading to the Williams Fork Reservoir. Getting there, however, is tricky. It is strongly suggested, once in town, that you ask someone for exact directions and information related to any collecting restrictions you might encounter due to private property and questionable river access. The vagueness related to accessing Williams Fork Road is because the author has not yet actually collected there. Due to its fine reputation and close proximity to the Colorado River sites, however, it seemed foolish not to mention it.

The Colorado River near Parshall

PARSHALL

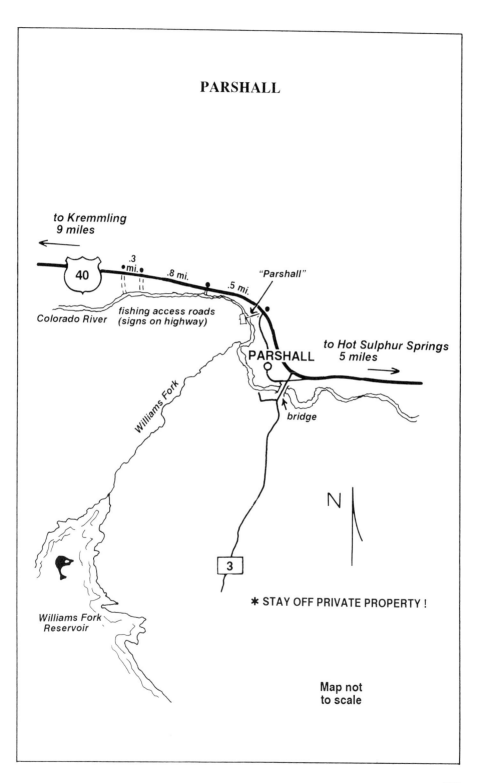

to Kremmling
9 miles

40

.3
mi.

.8 mi.

.5 mi.

"Parshall"

Colorado River

fishing access roads
(signs on highway)

PARSHALL

to Hot Sulphur Springs
5 miles

Williams Fork

bridge

N

3

Williams Fork
Reservoir

✻ STAY OFF PRIVATE PROPERTY !

Map not
to scale

Good quality gypsum can be gathered from the hills situated between the Wyoming border and Fort Collins. To get to the most accessible portion of this vast collecting area, head north from Fort Collins on Highway 287 about eighteen miles to where County Road 72 intersects from the east. Turn and go only a few tenths of a mile to where some low lying hills can be spotted just north of the road. Conspicuous, bright, white veins of gypsum will be seen layered throughout the hills. The thickness of the veins ranges from very thin to many feet in width.

Most of the material is bright white, but some multi-colored chunks in hues of pink, green, orange and tan can also be gathered. Thick solid pieces can be used for carving, and such material is generally referred to as alabaster. This soft, but pleasant-appearing mineral has been used throughout the world as a carving stone for countless centuries. After you have had a chance to work with it, you will see why. It looks hard, but is deceptively soft, and requires little effort to work and polish.

Unlike many gypsum collecting locations, material gathered here tends to be very solid, void of the usual internal fracturing and inclusions. Sizable pieces can be spotted just lying on the ground, but the very largest and least weathered must be dug directly from the veins in the hillsides. Hard rock tools will be needed to procure material from the hills, but, due to the softness, it is relatively easy to remove.

When digging, be on the lookout for cavities, since some contain spectacular crystals, occasionally reaching lengths of many inches. Again, the gypsum is very fragile, and if you do come upon an especially nice crystal cavity, great care must be taken when removing it. Try to extract as sizable a portion of the host rock as possible. After removal, carefully trim it to a more manageable size. In addition, be certain to wrap and securely store such pieces, since an unexpected bump could destroy everything.

About one more mile from the first stop, and continuing for about another mile, additional collecting opportunities are available. Park off the road, crawl under the highway fence, and hike through the gullies and alongside the hills looking for the veins.

This is grazing land, so please do not damage the fence when crawling through. Most of what can be found here, as was the case before, is solid and clean. Chunks of satin spar, a striated form of selenite, can also be picked up here. Such specimens, when cut and polished, can produce spectacular stones displaying a "billowing" chatoyancy. Occasional flattened calcite crystals will also be encountered, and they, if well formed, are nice for display in mineral collections.

OWL CANYON GYPSUM

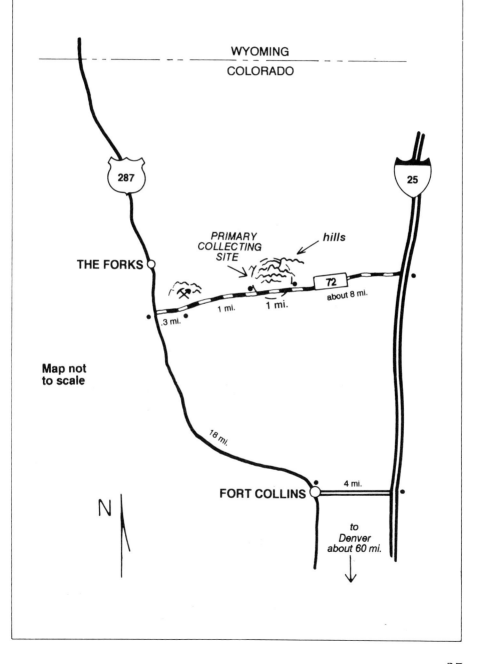

This may not be the most productive collecting site described in the book, but it is certainly one of the most scenic. The primary collecting site is situated on the banks of Green Mountain Reservoir, about seventeen miles south of Kremmling. It is centered within some intriguing black shale deposits.

Probably the safest and best access to the shale is on the west side of Highway 9, one-half mile north of milepost 122. The pullout is easily spotted when heading north. It is a good-sized clearing immediately south and adjacent to a substantial road cut through the black shale. Just be careful when turning left on this busy highway, since most people will not be expecting to come upon a stopped car. The turnout can't be seen until you're completely through the road cut when accessing the site from the north.

The black shale is interesting, but most is very fragile and crumbly. Within the shale one can find tiny fossilized mollusks, but it takes a great deal of patience and care to obtain anything worth keeping. Use a sharp, thin knife to split the fragile shale along a bedding plane and carefully examine the freshly exposed surface for traces of the ancient sea life. Since the fossils are virtually the same color as the host shale, they do not stand out prominently and it takes some careful scrutiny to detect them.

This location also offers an opportunity to procure some interesting wonder stone-like material. It is found in association with the shale and contains brown, black, and orange bands and swirls. Most pieces are quite porous and thereby not capable of taking a high gloss polish. An occasional piece will produce a dull gloss if worked carefully and selectively. Choice, unpolished pieces are nice for display in a mineral collection, as they were found, trimmed to exhibit the best color contrasts.

There are additional deposits of the easily-spotted black shale along Highway 9 extending a few miles both to the north and to the south. Any of them offer equal potential for nice collectibles. Just be certain you pull completely off this busy highway wherever you choose to park.

The primary collecting site at Green Mountain Reservoir

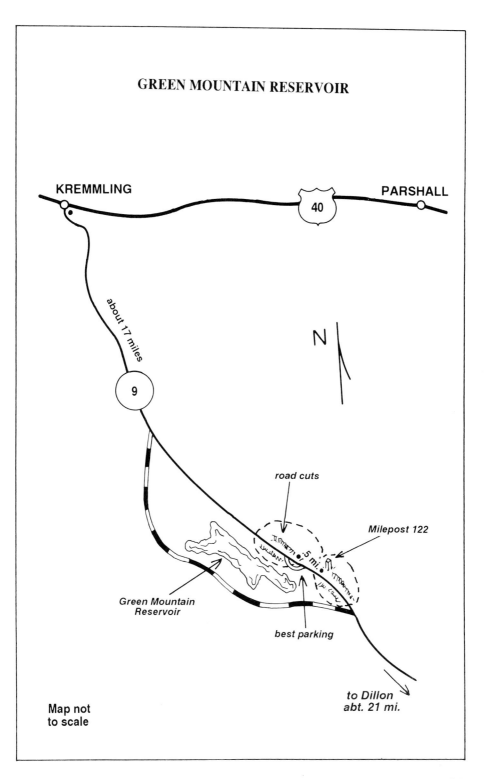

GREEN MOUNTAIN RESERVOIR

KREMMLING

PARSHALL

40

about 17 miles

9

N

road cuts

Milepost 122

.5 mi.

Green Mountain
Reservoir

best parking

to Dillon
abt. 21 mi.

Map not
to scale

29

This is a renowned collecting site, providing the rockhound an opportunity to gather chunks of some of the most pure, bright, white marble available anywhere. This historic location provided the high quality material that was used for construction of the Lincoln Memorial and the Tomb of the Unknown Soldier. In fact, the 124-ton marble base for the Tomb was the largest single chunk of marble ever excavated anywhere.

The collecting is centered about the town of Marble, situated among some of Colorado's finest ski resorts. Obviously, you should not attempt collecting during the colder winter months since the ground is often covered with snow. To get there, head south from Glenwood Springs, on Highway 82, toward Aspen. After having gone about twelve miles, bear right onto Highway 133 and proceed another twenty-two and six-tenths miles. At that point, on the east, is the marked turnoff to Marble, where you should continue five and one-half miles to town.

All along the approach, specimens of the brilliant white marble can be seen alongside the road. It might be worthwhile to stop and examine some of these pieces in an effort to get a sense for what the local material looks like. Today, only a handful of people inhabit the once prosperous town. During its heyday, the mine supported over 1500 people. If you have a rugged four-wheel drive unit, it is possible to visit the actual quarry, which is situated in the hills about four miles farther along, but passenger cars cannot make the trip. This is a fascinating place to visit, and it is interesting to see the site of what was once the world's largest marble finishing mill. Be advised, however, that collecting is not allowed in the quarry itself, since mining is currently being conducted.

The deposit was discovered in 1890 and most mining ceased in 1941, with a brief spurt again in 1953. The broken columns, huge blocks and other partially formed chunks of the brilliant white marble formulate a most unusual landscape, so be sure to take your camera along.

Specimens can be gathered just about anywhere in the region. The roadbeds are supported with crushed marble and the streams are full of it. Large chunks can be spotted all along the roads where they must have fallen off overloaded trucks. Do not trespass onto private property and stay off any active claim.

Larger polished pieces can be made from this material, with clock faces, bookends and carvings being among the most popular. Gathering minerals here is no problem. Don't just drive in, fill up you car with marble, and drive out, though. Spend a little time exploring the town, and, if you can get to it, the old mine. You won't regret having done so.

MARBLE

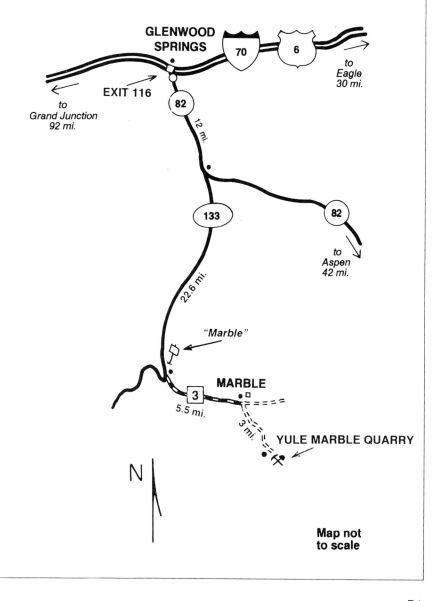

This is one of Colorado's prime rhodochrosite producing sites. The beautiful, vivid red specimens emanating from this locality are prized possessions in many private and museum collections throughout the world. Collecting is centered about the Sweet Home Mine, a PRIVATE and sporadically active prospect. DO NOT, under any circumstances, trespass on the mine property without first securing permission to do so. Current ownership status can be obtained from the county offices in nearby Fairplay. If you are unable to contact the mine owners for permission to explore the Sweet Home dumps, or do not have the time to do so, restrict your collecting to regions beyond the claims.

To get to this well-known and scenic location, proceed to the small town of Alma by taking Highway 9 six miles north of Fairplay. Once in Alma, go west on County Road 8 toward Kite Lake. Go four more miles to where you will pass directly between one of the Sweet Home Mine dumps and a small building.

Interesting specimens of agate, jasper and occasional rhodochrosite can be found along the banks of nearby Buckskin Creek. Additional specimens can be picked up in some of the numerous abandoned dumps which can be seen as you proceed toward Kite Lake. If in doubt as to whether or not they are abandoned, search on the hillsides directly below, since erosion will have probably washed some specimens from where they were discarded at the higher elevations.

This entire region, starting about 3 miles west of Alma and continuing all the way to Kite Lake, provides lots of fine collecting opportunities. Since some of the dumps are situated high on the surrounding hillsides, be very careful if planning to hike them. The footing is frequently unstable, and the climb is potentially exhausting. This would be a remote place to become injured.

Specimens of pyrite can be picked up on the dump of the old abandoned mine at Kite Lake, and the drive is most scenic. Even if you don't find much, this pleasant Colorado mountain trek will be well worth your time.

View of the collecting area

ALMA RHODOCHROSITE

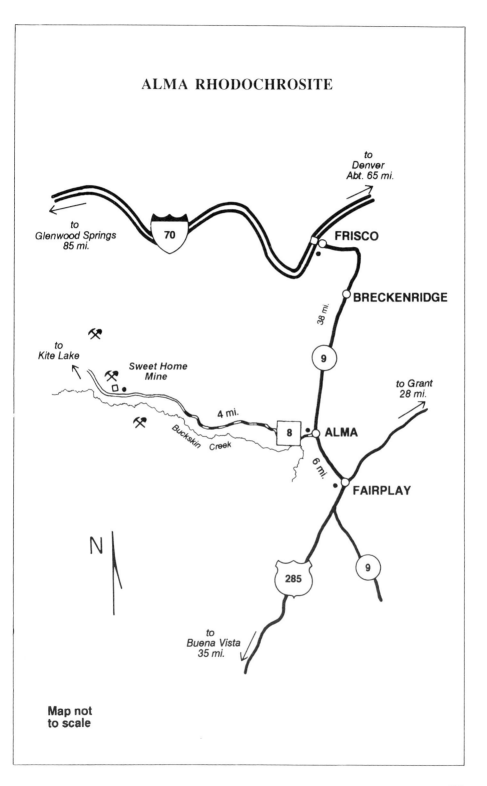

to
Denver
Abt. 65 mi.

to
Glenwood Springs
85 mi.

70

FRISCO

BRECKENRIDGE

38 mi.

9

to
Kite Lake

Sweet Home
Mine

to Grant
28 mi.

4 mi.

Buckskin Creek

8

ALMA

6 mi.

FAIRPLAY

N

285

9

to
Buena Vista
35 mi.

**Map not
to scale**

The accompanying map illustrates some of the major mines near Leadville where fine mineral specimens have been found. Due to the nature of mining claims, however, no particular specific mine or dump is discussed.

A mine that was open to collecting a week ago may be closed today, and vice-versa. Rather than create frustration by directing collectors to specific prospects in this still active mining region, the author has chosen to illustrate some of the major mines and briefly discuss what type of minerals are available.

If you cannot determine a specific mine's collecting status, try checking in town either at the Chamber of Commerce or at a city government building. If you do not want to go to that trouble, a drive through this historically significant area is still fascinating and picturesque. In addition, many of the dumps extend down to the roadways where collectors can gather minerals. Erosion has also carried many fine specimens from the mines into streambeds, washes and other low lying areas. Take time to explore those places and you may be well rewarded.

Minerals found in the Leadville mines include aragonite, calcite, cerussite, galena, gold, hemimorphite, psilomelane, purite, pyromorphite, quartz, siderite, silver, and sphalerite.

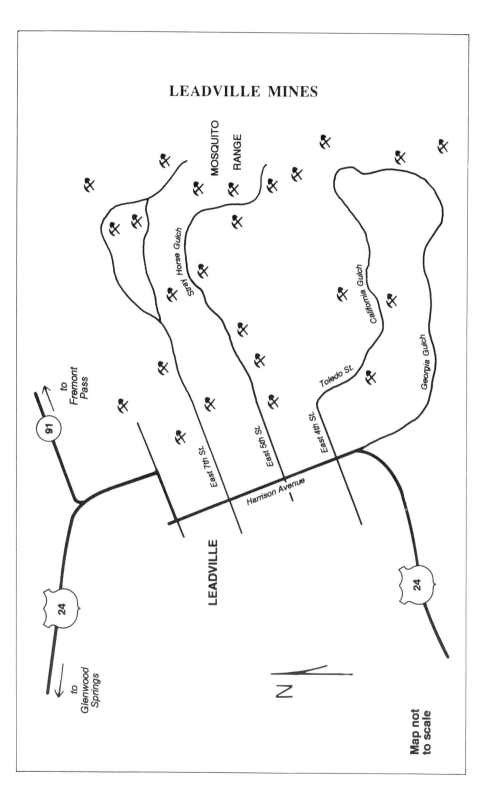

LEADVILLE MINES

MOSQUITO RANGE

Stray Horse Gulch

California Gulch

Georgia Gulch

Toledo St.

East 4th St.

East 5th St.

East 7th St.

Harrison Avenue

LEADVILLE

to Fremont Pass

91

24

to Glenwood Springs

24

N

Map not to scale

Many Colorado collectors feel that the jasper and agate found just north of the tiny town of Raymer is the finest available anywhere in the entire state. The site features a clean brown jasper, as well as red, yellow and black varieties, most of which is very solid and takes a great polish. The real prize, however, is that which is filled with delicate, colorful and often intricate bands.

To get to this well-known location, start in Raymer, which is situated on Highway 14 about two miles west of where Highway 52 intersects. From town, take Road 129 north, twelve and eight-tenths miles. At that point, on the left, you will encounter an abandoned building, which is all that remains of the small town of Kalouse. Park off the main road and hike in any direction. There is a hill, illustrated on the accompanying map, which has provided lots of fine material in years past. Specimens can also be gathered by hiking along any of the intersecting roads for quite a distance.

Much of the property in this region is private ranch land, including the hill mentioned earlier. If gates are locked, or if no trespassing signs are posted, do not enter that particular area. Gathering minerals alongside the roads is allowed, and excellent specimens can be procured in that manner. In fact, due to the frequent grading, new pieces are continually being exposed. Look on the roads themselves, as well as areas of erosion just off the graded stretches.

This site is particularly productive after a rainstorm, but the high clay content of the native soil can make the trip treacherous. Unless you have a vehicle designed to travel on such roads and are willing to have your shoes virtually encased in soft gooey clay, it is best to only explore here in dry weather. It should also be pointed out that concentrations of the jasper and agate vary considerably. Be patient and willing to do some walking and you can determine for yourself if the Kalouse jasper/agate field provides the best Colorado has to offer.

Abandoned building marking the start of the collecting area

RAYMER JASPER

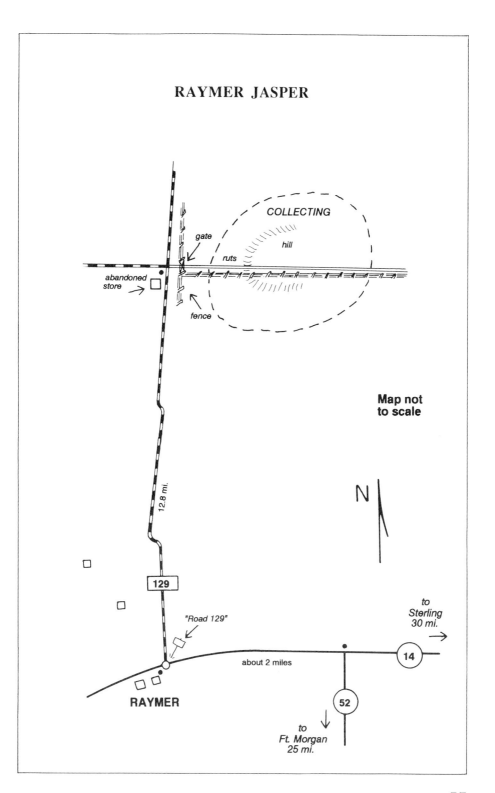

COLLECTING

hill

gate

ruts

abandoned
store

fence

Map not
to scale

N

12.8 mi.

129

"Road 129"

to
Sterling
30 mi.

about 2 miles

14

RAYMER

52

to
Ft. Morgan
25 mi.

This is generally regarded as one of Colorado's most famous mineral collecting sites. The clear blue barite crystals that have been found here are prized pieces in displays throughout the world.

The site is situated in Colorado's somewhat remote northeast corner. To get there from Fort Morgan, go north on Highway 52 to its intersection with Highway 14. Turn right and drive seven miles to where Highway 71 branches north at the tiny borough of Stoneham. Go east another one and one-tenth miles and turn north onto well-graded County Road 149.

After having traveled about two miles, on the left a road leads to the property owner's home, nestled in a grove of trees. You should stop there and obtain permission to visit the collecting area. The site has been closed periodically in the past due to thoughtless rockhounds. Be certain that you adhere to the owner's requests. Basically, he asks that you only use hand tools, fill any holes you dig, and don't leave trash on his property.

Continue north from the house until you have gone three and one-tenth miles from the highway. At that point, bear right on the main road, cross the cattle guard, and proceed another nine-tenths of a mile. From there, go right onto the ruts six-tenths of a mile farther to the edge of the site.

On the flat highlands, occasional pieces of agate and jasper can be found, but the mineral of interest here is the blue barite which is gathered in the light colored cliffs and washes north of the road. The crystals can be picked up loose from the colored soil where they have been eroded from the shale, or they can be extracted directly from the cavities where they were formed.

The easiest collecting procedure is to walk through the low-lying regions. The crystals are easy to spot, since their bright blue color vividly stands out against the pale soil, but these eroded specimens tend to be fractured and small.

If you try extracting them from the cavities in the shale, look for yellow or white calcite, which frequently lines the barite-bearing cracks and crevices. Then very carefully try to remove as large a portion of the surrounding host rock as possible. The crystals are often terminated, sometimes on both ends, and lengths of well over an inch are not uncommon.

Blue barite from regions north and south of Stoneham

STONEHAM BLUE BARITE

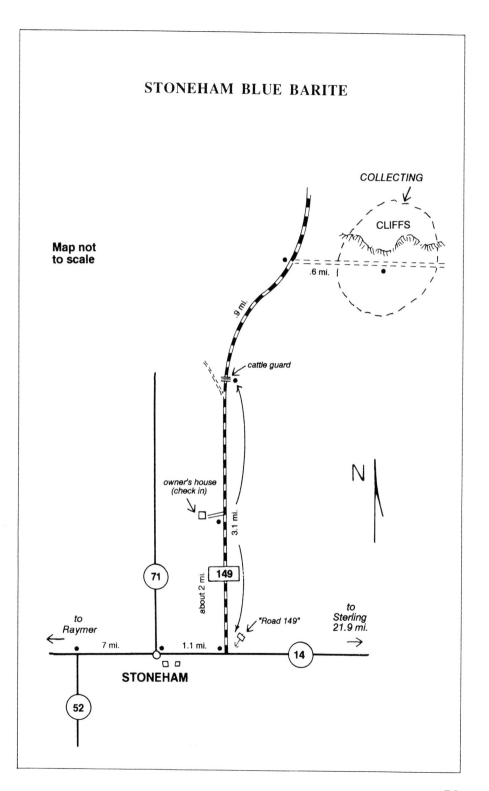

Perry Park is a small community nestled amongst red sandstone cliffs, unusual geological formations, and a beautiful little lake. In fact, this collecting site is situated just across the street from the community golf course and boasts good samples of both satin spar and alabaster.

To get to this unusual locality, travel fifteen miles south from Sedalia, on Highway 105, to the Red Rock Road turnoff, or take Exit 173 from Interstate 25, in Larkspur, and go northwest approximately nine miles, as shown on the map. In any event, no matter which route you choose, go northwest two and one-tenth miles on Red Rock Road to Perry Park. At the given mileage, the road ends at a stop sign and you should turn right, going only two-tenths of a mile farther.

From there, and continuing approximately one-half mile, on the right, collectors can locate seams of high quality satin spar, a striated, fibrous variation of selenite, and good clean white alabaster, a more dense and granular gypsum variant. The simplest way to collect here is to park in the golf course parking area and walk across the street. If you prefer, however, it is also possible to pull off the pavement immediately next to some of the hills.

Specimens can be picked up amongst the rubble next to the road, but the finest, least weathered and damaged material is obtained by scrambling up the hills to an actual seam and carefully removing a good-sized portion directly from where it was formed. The encasing soil is not especially hard, so extracting the gypsum is relatively easy. Be very careful not to knock rocks onto the road and try not to damage what you remove, since it is quite fragile and easily scratched.

Try collecting at a number of spots along the one-half mile stretch of hills, to get a sampling of what the site has to offer.

A gypsum-bearing hill at the site

PERRY PARK

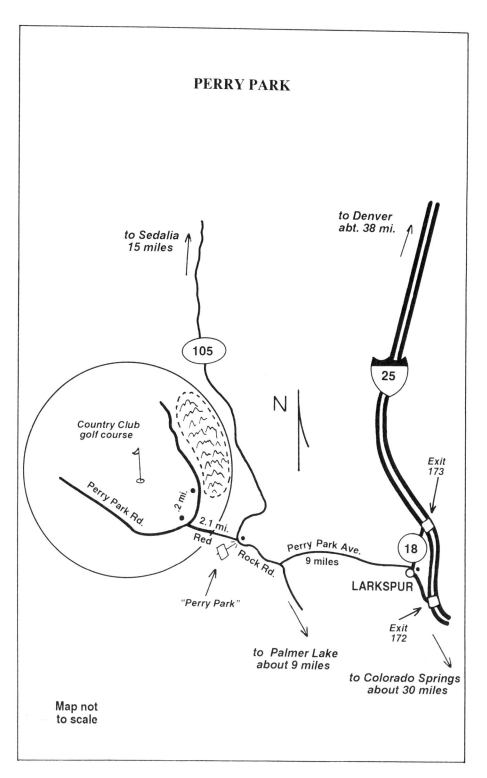

to Sedalia
15 miles

to Denver
abt. 38 mi.

105

N

25

Country Club
golf course

Perry Park Rd.

.2 mi.

2.1 mi.

Red

Rock Rd.

Perry Park Ave.
9 miles

Exit
173

18

LARKSPUR

"Perry Park"

to Palmer Lake
about 9 miles

Exit
172

to Colorado Springs
about 30 miles

Map not
to scale

Excellent quartz specimens can be obtained at this highly productive location situated in the mountainous region to the southwest of Sedalia. The site boasts, among other things, delicate terminated crystals, water clear quartz, black biotite mica, feldspar, and some extremely clean smoky quartz.

To get there, from Sedalia, head west out of town, on Highway 67, ten miles and then turn south onto Rampart Range Road, toward Devil's Head. The turnoff to the Devil's Head lookout tower will be encountered after having gone eight and six-tenths miles from the highway, but you should bear straight ahead on the main road. Topaz Point will be passed one and nine-tenths miles farther. Four and three-tenths miles past Topaz Point is Site B. Site B is easily spotted from the road and consists of a series of quartz outcrops on the right, among the trees.

These pegmatites offer feldspar crystals and other associated minerals. Park off the road and inspect as many as you desire. The best material is obtained by using a sledge hammer, gads and chisels, to split into the deposit, in an effort to expose unweathered crystals. Site C is reached by continuing down the road another four-tenths of a mile to some ruts which head right through more pegmatite outcrops, similar to those at Site B.

The primary collecting area, Site A, is accessed by driving three-tenths of a mile farther south from Site C, to Road 348. Go west one-half mile to where ruts will be seen heading off to the right. The ruts are white, being covered with chips and boulders of brilliantly colored quartz. The short climb up to the quarry is steep, but most rugged vehicles should have no problem.

Fine quartz specimens can be picked up throughout these old workings, but the best is found by following the washed out road into the main quarry. Huge boulders are strewn about, and hard rock tools can be used to split them in hopes of exposing a crystal-filled cavity. Be VERY CAREFUL if you choose to work on the quarry walls, since colossal boulders precariously hang from upper ledges, and it wouldn't take much to dislodge one.

Site A

FERN CREEK

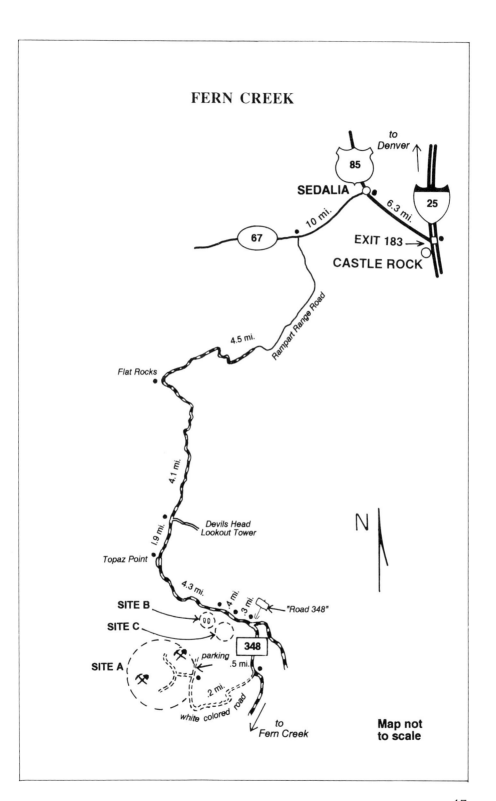

Some of the best topaz crystal collecting in the entire state of Colorado is in a somewhat condensed region near the Devil's Head lookout tower, a few miles southwest of Sedalia. The main site is on what used to be a private claim governed by the Colorado Mineral Society, but, at the time of publication, the claim was released and no longer protected. This status, as is the case with any mineral claim, is subject to change, however.

To get to this renowned site from Sedalia, take Highway 67 ten miles west from town and then turn south onto Rampart Range Road, continuing another eight and six-tenths miles to the Devil's Head Campground turnoff. Proceed straight ahead another one and eight-tenths miles to where faint tracks can be seen leading off to the left. Those tracks lead to Site A, the old CMS claim. If you get to the Topaz Point rest station, you have passed the turnoff and should double back one-tenth of a mile.

The ruts leading to Site A are rough. If you have any concerns as to whether your vehicle can make the short journey to the digging area, park at Topaz Point and hike in. Pits will be seen after having gone one-tenth of a mile from the main road and they are scattered throughout the trees for quite a distance. Most are overgrown, eroded, and partially filled in. The topaz can be obtained by screening the soft soil or by directly attacking the host rock, in hopes of exposing a crystal-bearing cavity.

Site B, centered around Topaz Point, offers additional good hunting. The region between the rest station and Virgin's Bath is filled with potentially productive pegmatites. Everything from beautiful smoky quartz and topaz crystals to colorful feldspar can be found. Obviously, it takes some concentrated searching and a little luck to get the best this locality has to offer. Screening soil in the valley across the road from Topaz Point also provides rockhounds topaz crystals and is worth exploring.

Searching for a crystal-bearing cavity, Site B

DEVIL'S HEAD

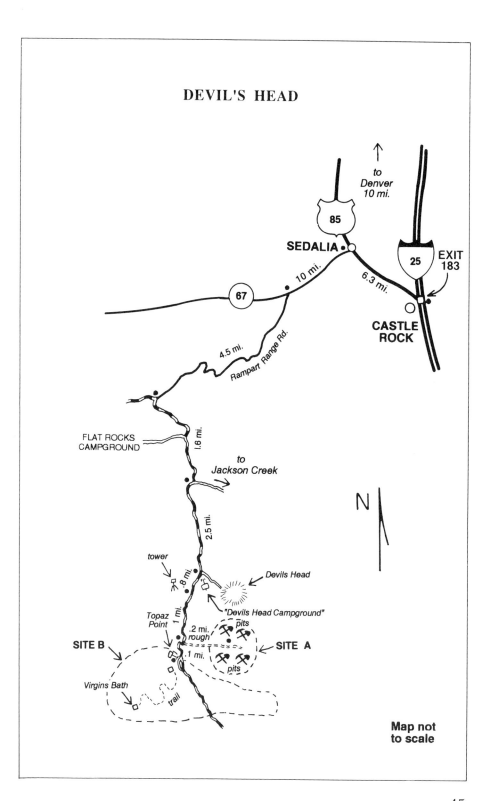

to
Denver
10 mi.

85

SEDALIA

25   EXIT
183

10 mi.

6.3 mi.

67

CASTLE
ROCK

4.5 mi.

Rampart Range Rd.

FLAT ROCKS
CAMPGROUND

1.6 mi.

to
Jackson Creek

N

2.5 mi.

tower

.8 mi.

Devils Head

"Devils Head Campground"

Topaz
Point

1 mi.

.2 mi.
rough

pits

SITE B

1 mi.

SITE A

pits

Virgins Bath

trail

**Map not
to scale**

The entire region southwest of Sedalia is renowned for the fine mineral specimens that can be found there. This location is no exception. To get there, take Exit 183 from Interstate 25, in Castle Rock, and follow Highway 85 six and three-tenths miles to Sedalia. From there, go left onto County Road 67 and drive thirteen and four-tenths miles to the small community of Pine Creek.

Throughout much of the surrounding region there are numerous pegmatite exposures which have provided collectors with excellent crystal specimens over the years. Of particular interest are fine examples of smoky quartz, amazonite, and feldspar. One particularly promising area is illustrated on the accompanying map, but it certainly isn't the only place that minerals can be found.

To get there from town, take County Road 67 four-tenths of a mile to Pine Creek Lane, which is encountered just after passing over a small bridge. At that intersection, and continuing in all directions, there are numerous pegmatites. Careful examination of the deposits themselves, as well as material that has been weathered off, can lead to nice crystals. Nothing is overly plentiful, but good pieces can be found.

It is important to note that there is a lot of private property in the Pine Creek area, and, as is always the case, do not trespass unless you first get permission to do so. It might prove to be helpful to stop at the Pine Creek store for assistance and suggestions. Keep in mind that many of the local citizens have had unpleasant experiences with rockhounds who have cut or damaged fences, dug deep holes and not refilled them, knocked rocks onto roads, or left trash. As is the case with just about any other minerally productive region centered within or adjacent to private property, the thoughtlessness of previous visitors often comes back to haunt us.

Even if you are unable to find much at Pine Creek, the trip takes you through some beautiful mountainous regions and the scenery alone should make the trip worthwhile.

A road cut through crystal-bearing pegmatite rock

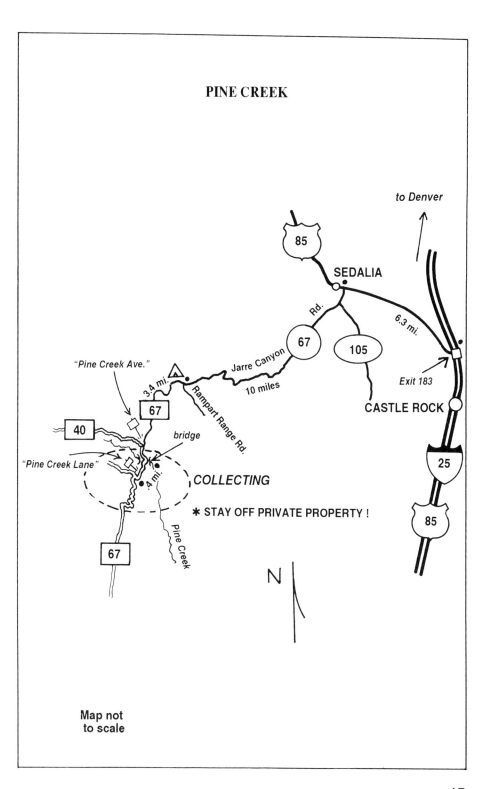

PINE CREEK

to Denver

85

SEDALIA

67

105

6.3 mi.

"Pine Creek Ave."

Jarre Canyon Rd.

10 miles

Rampart Range Rd.

3.4 mi.

67

Exit 183

CASTLE ROCK

40

bridge

"Pine Creek Lane"

.4 mi.

COLLECTING

* STAY OFF PRIVATE PROPERTY !

25

85

67

Pine Creek

N

Map not
to scale

North and South Table Mountains, prominently situated on the outskirts of Golden, offer collectors some of the best zeolite specimens available anywhere in Colorado. The problem with collecting here is that virtually all of the accessible land surrounding these two lofty mesas is on private property, thereby blocking access to the mineral-bearing volcanic rock high on the hillsides. Easley Road used to provide the best access, but a new housing project on the western slopes, when completed, may provide roads leading higher up the mountain with better accessibility.

This site is mentioned because of its mineralogical significance and because landowners do periodically allow rockhounds passage through their property if given the courtesy of being asked for permission to do so in advance. DO NOT, under any circumstances, trespass. Ask for authorization to enter.

The zeolites are found in cavities in the upper basalt regions of both South Table Mountain and North Table Mountain. Be very careful when hiking on these steep hills, since footing is occasionally unstable and, in some places, the drop is considerable. If you do get permission to explore either of the mesas, be sure to pack hard rock tools, and take along something to drink. It is a demanding and challenging hike to the crystal-bearing basalt, and once there the labor does not cease.

The tough volcanic host rock must be split in hopes of exposing crystal-bearing cavities. This involves lots of work. Use gads, chisels and sledge hammers, and be sure to wear goggles and gloves when conducting your excavations. The very finest specimens are obtained as a result of lots of hard work, determination, persistence and luck, not necessarily in that order! When you do extract a chunk of the basalt containing a zeolite-filled cavity, it is essential that you adequately wrap it to protect the often fragile crystals from damage when being transported back down the hillside.

The view from the higher elevations is spectacular, and if you are able to gather some mineral specimens, that view helps to make the trek more enjoyable and memorable.

Tourmaline and mica in feldspar

GOLDEN ZEOLITES

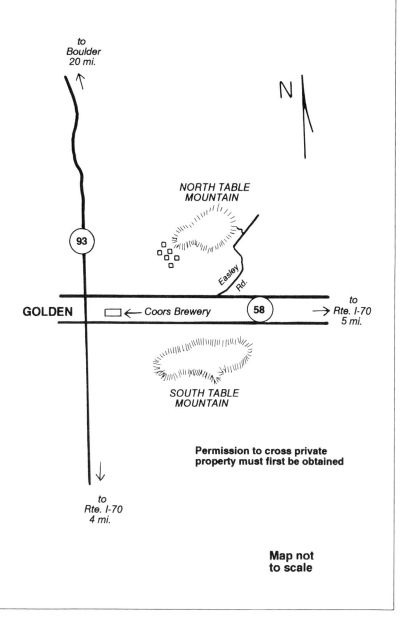

to
Boulder
20 mi.

N

NORTH TABLE
MOUNTAIN

93

Easley Rd.

GOLDEN ☐← Coors Brewery 58 → Rte. I-70
5 mi.
to

SOUTH TABLE
MOUNTAIN

**Permission to cross private
property must first be obtained**

to
Rte. I-70
4 mi.

**Map not
to scale**

These two locations offer collectors a good selection of nice crystalized pegmatite minerals. To get to Site A, start in Golden and proceed north on Highway 93 one and four-tenths miles from where the arch crosses over Washington Street in the middle of town. From there, turn left onto Golden Gate Canyon Road and travel an additional six and three-tenths miles.

At that point, on the right, continuing alongside the road for at least another one-half mile, numerous pegmatite outcrops will be seen. In fact, the road cuts directly through some of them, and the deposit is very easy to spot since the mica sparkles brightly in the sunlight. Throughout these pegmatites, colorful feldspar crystals, mica books and black tourmaline can be gathered.

If you don't have much luck at the first stop, walk or drive a little farther and try again. Breaking up the pegmatite with hard rock tools such as gads and sledge hammers is sometimes very helpful in exposing otherwise hidden specimens. In addition, the freshly exposed material tends to be of better quality than that which has been subjected to weathering.

From Site A, continue on Golden Gate Canyon Road another one and three-tenths miles to where Robinson Hill Road intersects on the left. Robinson Hill Road cuts directly through a massive pegmatite, just past the intersection, and affords collectors additional specimens. This is Site B, and, as was the case at Site A, books of mica, black tourmaline crystals and feldspar in shades of orange, brown and yellow can be found. Some of the mica is very clean and sizeable, making excellent display pieces for a mineral collection, especially if attached to colorful feldspar.

Be careful when collecting at Site B, since this is a road cut and the bank is quite steep. If you start digging in the lower regions, it is possible that you may dislodge material from higher up. In addition, be certain that nothing rolls onto the roadway.

Collecting at Site A

GOLDEN GATE TOURMALINE

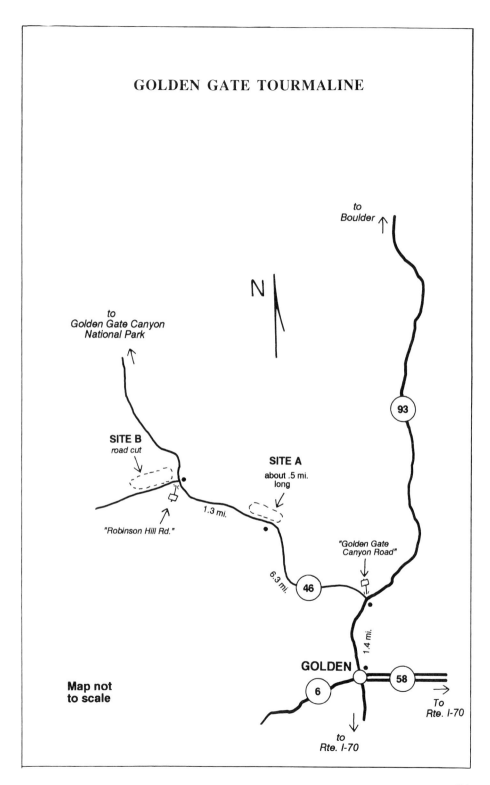

51

Coal probably does not cause a lot of excitement to rockhounds, but this particular coal deposit has a little something extra which might activate some curiosity. It is here at the Leyden Coal Mine, situated a short distance north of Golden, where the radioactive mineral carnotite was discovered in the mid-1800s.

Specimens of the colorful yellow carnotite can still be found here, and, even though it can't be cut and polished, choice pieces do make interesting additions to mineral collections. To get to this historic old mine, head north from Golden on Highway 93 about six and six-tenths miles to the Leyden turnoff. There, just north of the intersection, is the old mine.

The carnotite is easily spotted, primarily occurring in the form of brilliant yellow deposits on much of the native rocks of the quarry. Additional carnotite will be seen on some of the rocks just south of Leyden Road.

The most accessible carnotite has, for all practical purposes, already been removed. Nice specimens can be obtained on the higher elevations of the quarry and surrounding cliffs. Be extremely careful if you choose to go after that higher up material.

Due to potential health risks associated with radioactivity in some uranium ores, it is suggested that you do not carry specimens in your pockets and be certain to wash your hands after collecting. In addition, carrying a Geiger Counter might be interesting as well as helpful in avoiding areas of high radioactivity.

While at the mine, it is interesting to see the coal vein, and specimens of that more common mineral can readily be gathered. Be also advised, since this is a mining site, that collecting status is always subject to change. If you have any doubts regarding whether collecting is allowed, restrict your exploration to regions outside its boundaries or ascertain ownership status in Golden. Some nice specimens can be gathered in the area surrounding the quarry. A visit to this historic locality makes the trip worthwhile.

Leyden Coal Mine

LEYDEN COAL & URANIUM

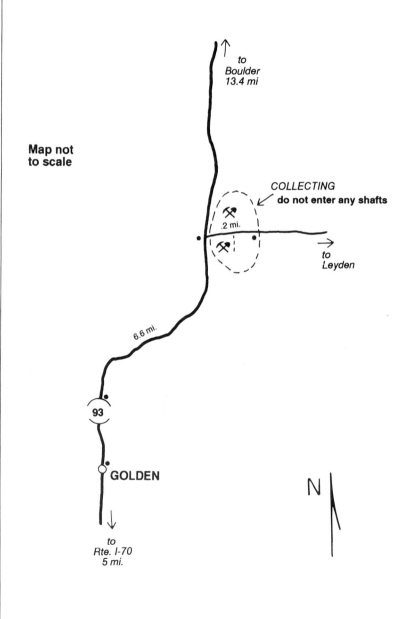

to
Boulder
13.4 mi

**Map not
to scale**

COLLECTING
← **do not enter any shafts**

.2 mi.

→
to
Leyden

6.6 mi.

93

GOLDEN

to
Rte. I-70
5 mi.

N

These three sites offer the collector lots of fine pegmatite minerals, including feldspar, tourmaline, mica and quartz crystals. To get to the first site, A, go north from Nederland on Highway 72 three and one-tenth miles from where Highway 119 intersects. At the given mileage, turn east onto Sugarloaf Sunset Road and proceed three and one-tenth miles to where an abandoned quarry will be encountered on the left.

Pull off the main road, park and explore the rubble for specimens. This is the once productive Oregon Mine, and chunks of ferberite, as well as occasional pieces of light pink fluorite can be obtained by the diligent collector. In addition, mica books and feldspar can be gathered with little difficulty. Be careful if exploring the quarry walls and do not enter the sealed shaft.

To get to Site B, continue along Sugarloaf Sunset Road another one-half mile and then go right onto Switzerland Park Road another four-tenths of a mile. At the given mileage, on the cliff overlooking the road on the left, an old abandoned mine will be spotted. It is difficult to find a good place to park here, and you may have to drive a short distance to locate a suitable spot. Rugged vehicles can pull off onto the ruts leading up to the rotting ore chute. In any event, do not block the road since it is used by local residents.

The trail leading up to the mine workings is overgrown but easily followed. Pegmatite specimens will be spotted throughout the brush and weeds along the way, as well as on the dump and lower lying regions. Having a bucket of water handy is also a good idea since the host soil seems to cling to the stones, making them difficult to identify. Washing will allow a much better evaluation of quality and color saturation.

Site C, our final spot, is reached by returning to Sugarloaf Sunset Road and going east another three-tenths of a mile. At that point, just as the road curves north, pegmatite boulders and outcrops will be seen among the trees to the left. Additional mica, feldspar and other related minerals can be found by searching the terrain or by breaking up the rocks.

NEDERLAND MINERALS

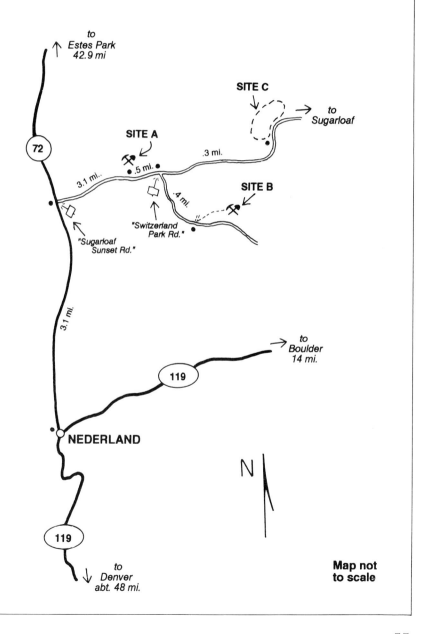

to
Estes Park
42.9 mi

SITE C

to
Sugarloaf

SITE A

72

.3 mi.

3.1 mi.

.5 mi.

SITE B

.4 mi.

"Switzerland
Park Rd."

"Sugarloaf
Sunset Rd."

3.1 mi.

to
Boulder
14 mi.

119

NEDERLAND

N

119

to
Denver
abt. 48 mi.

**Map not
to scale**

Nice specimens of massive blue barite crystals can be obtained in a relatively condensed region a short distance from Hartsel. To reach this well-known site, head west from Hartsel one and one-half miles on Highway 24 and turn south onto the well-graded road leading through the Hartsel Ranch housing development. Bear straight ahead and do not go onto any of the private side roads.

At time of publication, the Hartsel Ranch housing development was nothing more than some street signs and overgrown roads, but that may change. Be certain not to trespass if it appears to be active once again.

Drive one-half mile from the highway and go through the gate onto the ruts leading up through the shallow hills. After having passed through the gate, be certain to close it since cattle sometimes graze in this region. Continue eight-tenths of a mile farther, bearing right at the fork, to where pits will be seen on both sides of the road. It is in and around those pits where the chunks of sometimes vivid blue barite crystal clusters are found. If you bear left at the fork, you will encounter addtional pits, but, at time of publication, they are protected by a private mining claim. That region is more productive than the primary collecting site, but permission is only granted to groups requesting to visit well in advance. For information contact Golden Minerals, 13030 West Sixth Place, Golden, Colorado 80401.

The best method for obtaining the barite is to start digging in the somewhat soft soil of the pits. Since the dirt here is fine, the barite, when extracted, is hard to identify, other than it is somewhat heavier than you would expect a similar sized rock to be. It is usually quite helpful to have a pail of water in which you can dip any suspect stones to more accurately ascertain their true nature.

Most of the barite found in this location is blue, but the intensity of color does vary considerably. Obviously, the more saturated and brilliant the blue, and more defined the crystalline structure, the better. Most specimens, however, tend to be very pale, almost white.

There are quite a number of pits in the region, and all offer rockhounds good potential for procuring fine specimens. If you have the time, be sure to explore as many as possible.

Parked at the collecting site

ERRATA SHEET

GEM TRAILS OF COLORADO

GEM GUIDES BOOK COMPANY, 1997

Hartzel Blue Barite (Pages 56 - 57).
Permission to enter this site has been withdrawn by the Hartsel Ranch as it is now part of a buffalo herd grazing area.

HARTSEL BLUE BARITE

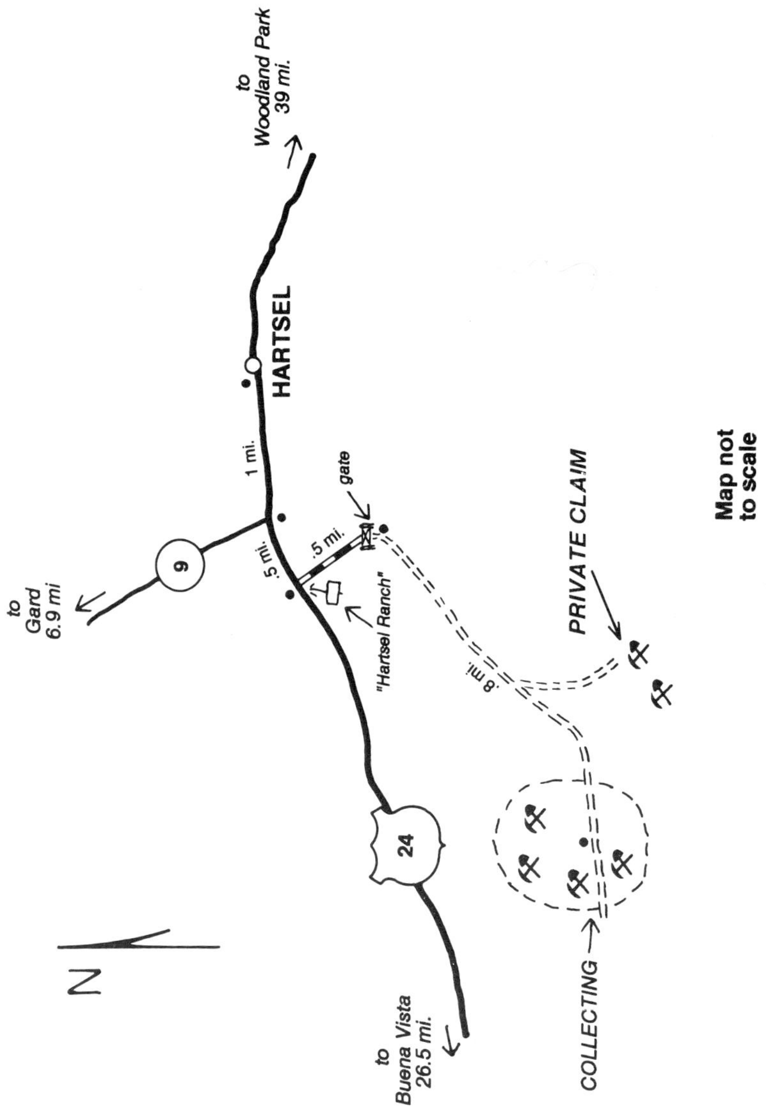

to
Woodland Park
39 mi.

HARTSEL

1 mi.

gate

to
Gard
6.9 mi

9

.5 mi.

.5 mi.

"Hartsel Ranch"

PRIVATE CLAIM

.8 mi.

Map not
to scale

24

to
Buena Vista
26.5 mi.

N

COLLECTING →

57

This site is very extensive, and a collector could spend days here inspecting all of the countless pegmatite and schist outcrops scattered throughout the landscape. The site is situated about midway between Hartsel and Lake George, on Highway 24. From Wilkerson Pass, go west two and one-half miles to County Road 23. Turn north onto the graded dirt road, and continue about two-tenths of a mile to the start of the site. From that point, stretching literally for miles, you will see numerous rocky outcrops jetting up from the flatlands. The outcrops are, for the most part, the source of the numerous minerals which can be found here.

The list of what can be obtained is extensive, but minerals of primary abundance and desirability include garnet, mica (clear and black), black tourmaline, scheelite, epidote, copper oxides, sphalerite, galena and some colorful feldspar. Most are found in the schist, which can be seen just about everywhere within the site's "boundaries."

Some specimens can be picked up from surface terrain, scattered randomly for miles. The best tends to be obtained by selecting a promising outcrop and breaking it down with gads, sledge hammer and chisels. Chunks of schist lying loose throughout the flatlands tend to be very weathered, thereby limiting their chances of containing well-formed, sharp, included crystals. Don't rule these smaller float pieces out entirely, though. If you do not have the hard rock tools, a simple prospector's pick can break up the smaller stones, and, occasionally, nice crystals will be exposed.

This is an easy place to explore. The area is fairly flat, and the schist outcrops are virtually unlimited. A bucket of water and a small magnifying glass may prove to be useful in identifying minerals and ascertaining their quality. Do not be hesitant to drive toward the mountains as far as you desire. Locations which are less accessible and/or farther from the main highway generally provide a better opportunity for more easily locating good specimens.

Searching for specimens

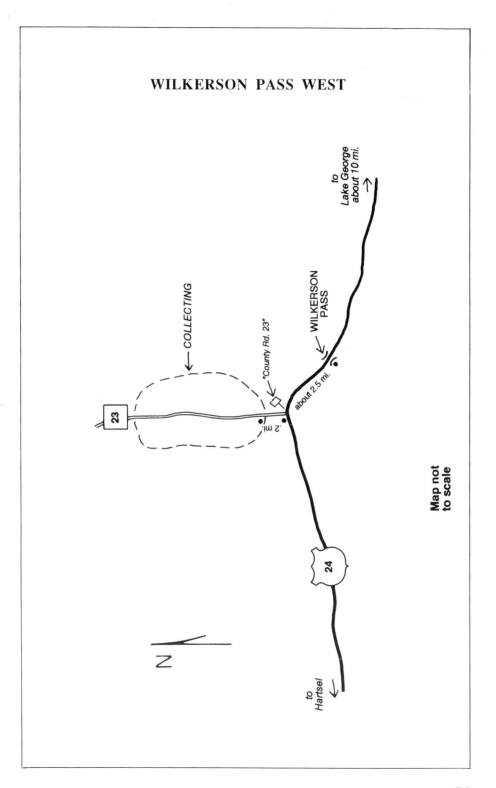

WILKERSON PASS WEST

COLLECTING

"County Rd. 23"

WILKERSON PASS

about 2.5 mi.

.2 mi.

23

24

to
Lake George
about 10 mi.

to
Hartsel

N

Map not
to scale

59

The dumps and the hills surrounding this old mine can provide rockhounds with some very nice mineral specimens. To get there, go east one-half mile from Wilkerson Pass, which is located about midway between Hartsel and Lake George, on Highway 24. At that point, turn north onto the tracks leading toward the easily spotted mine on the side of the hill just next to the highway.

Copper ores can be found throughout the surrounding region, including malachite, azurite and bornite. None, however, is really thick enough to cut and polish, but some pieces are brilliantly colored and can be used as fine additions to a mineral collection. When exploring the mine area, do not, under any circumstances, enter any of the old shafts. The native rock is rotted, and cave-ins are highly likely.

In addition to the copper ores, collectors can also frequently gather fine specimens of galena, feldspar, epidote, garnet, scheelite and black tourmaline. Most of the tourmaline is not picked up in the mine area but, instead, throughout the surrounding hills. Look for schist outcrops and attack them with hard rock tools such as gads, chisels and sledge hammers in hopes of exposing worthwhile specimens.

There is lots to be found at this locality, but it does take some patience and considerable luck to obtain the very best it has to offer. Be willing to hike a little and to do some rock busting. If willing to make that commitment, chances are that you will be handsomely rewarded. Take a container of water along to help in the identification of potentially valuable specimens, since the sometimes elusive minerals are often difficult to spot until cleaned.

Road to the collecting area

WILKERSON PASS EAST

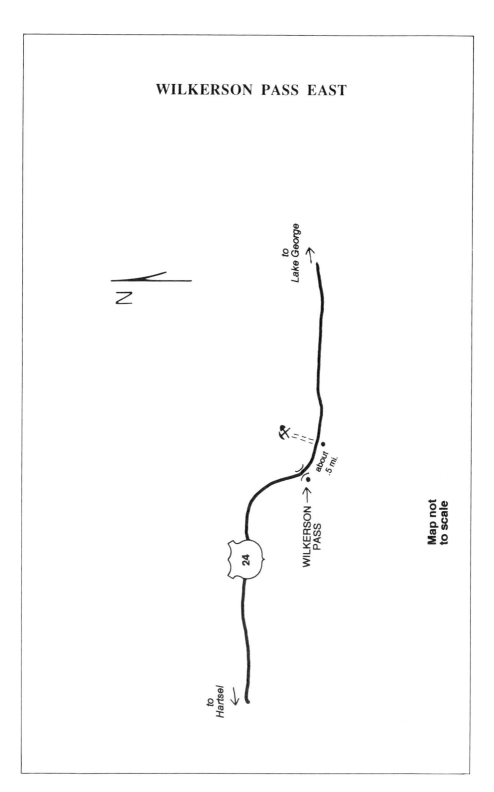

Map not
to scale

N

to
Lake George

WILKERSON →
PASS

about
.5 mi.

24

to
Hartsel

61

This deposit is known as the Teller Pegmatite and it provides collectors with a good selection of very nice mineral specimens. Be advised, however, that the quarry, itself, is flooded, thereby restricting which portions of the deposit you can explore.

To get there, take Eleven Mile Canyon Road south from the center of Lake George. Eleven Mile Canyon Road intersects Highway 24 at the post office, and is easily located once in town. Do not, however, get confused and proceed south on the road to Eleven Mile Reservoir, which intersects Highway 24 west of town. Go south only eight-tenths of a mile and pull off the road near the easily spotted diggings on the left. Lots of colorful pink and orange feldspar can be obtained here. If you are willing to do some splitting of boulders and breaking into the upper, accessible quarry walls, good mica, quartz and molybdenite can also be found.

The finest material from this location is generally regarded as pieces composed of well-colored feldspar showing crystal faces, in conjunction with thick and well-formed biotite mica books. Some, if properly trimmed, are spectacular for display in mineral collections.

Be very careful when exploring the Teller Pegmatite, since the drop into the quarry is steep and precarious. Do not attempt to scramble down into the flooded floor. It is extremely hazardous and difficult to get back out.

There are lots of good collecting opportunities alongside the quarry, especially above and behind it. Take a sledge hammer, some gads and chisels and attack the host rock to remove specimens which display the best crystal structure and possess the finest color. Once such pieces are removed, careful trimming, either at home or in the field, will help to accentuate the specimen's beauty.

Flooded quarry at the site

LAKE GEORGE PEGMATITE

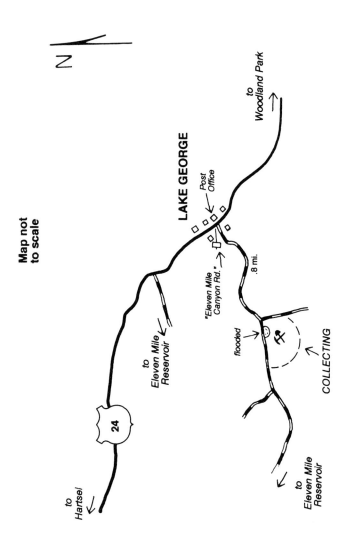

Map not
to scale

N

LAKE GEORGE

Post
Office

to
Woodland Park

"Eleven Mile
Canyon Rd."

.8 mi.

to
Eleven Mile
Reservoir

flooded

COLLECTING

24

to
Hartsel

to
Eleven Mile
Reservoir

Beautiful pink feldspar, idocrase, garnet, brilliant quartz, graphic granite and well-formed books of mica can all be found in a series of small prospects near prominent Round Mountain located only a few miles west of Lake George.

To get to the first, head west from Lake George on Highway 24 one and one-tenth miles to where County Road 77 intersects. Proceed another one and one-half miles. On the south side of the highway, about mid-way up the hill, a mine dump will be spotted. Access to this dump is difficult and involves parking off the pavement and hiking. If you have the energy and determination to get there, you should be able to gather specimens of orange and brown garnet crystals as well as an occasional green idocrase. There is also lots of pink feldspar and good, solid books of mica in and around the dump area.

If you don't feel like trekking all the way up to the hillside quarry, continue west on Highway 24 another two and nine-tenths miles to where a fairly well-graded road leads off to the north. If you get to Round Mountain Campground Road, you have passed the turn to the collecting sites and should double back. Once off the highway, go three-tenths of a mile to where the road splits, take either fork for one-tenth of a mile, and then turn right. Proceed another two-tenths of a mile to some pits on the right, partially obscured by trees and overburden. Search in and around those diggings for more feldspar, garnet and mica.

If you continue along the main road, numerous additional pits will be encountered, as will lots of pegmatite outcrops. If you have the time, it may prove fruitful to sample as many as possible. Take water to clean potential specimens in order to aid with identification and more accurately ascertain desirability. If your want to break up any of the numerous outcrops or larger boulders at the pits, it will be necessary to use sturdy hard rock tools.

Mica, quartz and feldspar

ROUND MOUNTAIN MINERALS

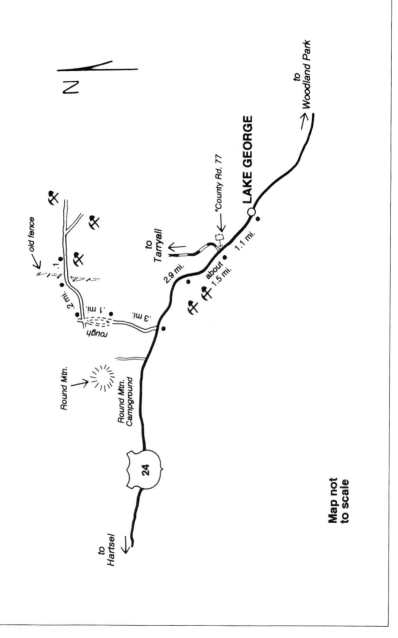

Map not
to scale

65

Some of Colorado's best topaz specimens can be found in the Tarryall Mining District, north of Lake George. To get there, take Highway 24 west from town one and one-tenth miles to County Road 77. Turn north and follow that well-graded dirt road eleven and seven-tenths miles to the tiny community of Tarryall.

Throughout the hills surrounding Tarryall, primarily west of the road, there are numerous mine dumps, and throughout those dumps one can occasionally find small topaz and quartz crystals. This region is designated as Site A on the map. If you choose to explore any of these dumps, be certain that you do not enter private property without first getting permission to do so and do not collect in any area where it is prohibited. More information can be obtained in Tarryall.

The most renown of the Tarryall collecting spots, designated as Site B on the map, is reached by proceeding another one and two-tenths miles to the Spruce Grove Campground, and parking in the lot designated for hikers. Before setting out on this somewhat strenuous one and one-half mile trek, be sure to take plenty of water, a sturdy bag for hauling supplies and specimens, hard rock tools, and some snacks. Be advised that the temperature can drop rapidly as the sun starts to set, so taking a jacket may also be wise.

Hike through the southern edge of the campground to the parking area, go through the logs, and follow the trail to the small footbridge which crosses the river. Once over the river, either go straight ahead past the picnic tables or follow the trail leading off to the left. Most collectors go straight, since that trail goes toward the southern part of Tarryall Peak, where there tends to be more consistent collecting. Outstanding specimens have also been found on northern Tarryall Peak, which is reached by the trail to the left.

The clear and blue topaz crystals grew in cavities within the pegmatite granite of Tarryall Peak. Removing them directly from their place in the mountainside is extremely difficult. Most people search for the crystals in the rubble below the rocky cliffs, alongside the many trails which circle the mountain. Either take a small screen with you to assist with examining the gravel or carefully inspect the smaller boulders for crystal-bearing cavities. Using a rock pick to split some of the more promising boulders in hopes of exposing otherwise concealed cavities is often well rewarded. Crystals removed directly from the host rock tend to be better formed and much cleaner, having not been exposed to the ravages of erosion and weather.

Do not set out on this hike unless you are physically fit, and do not climb onto high ridges from which you might fall. This location is many miles from help. In addition, be certain to start back to your vehicle well before day's end, since the trail is difficult to follow in the dark, and temperatures drop considerably.

66

TARRYALL TOPAZ

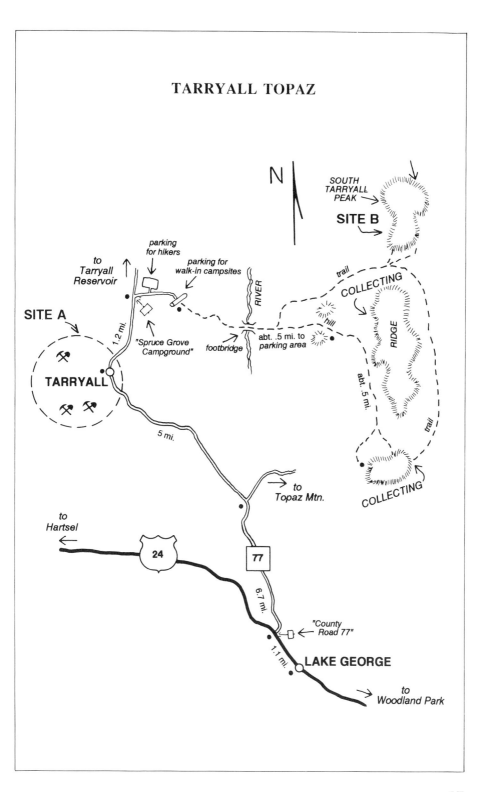

Region III—TOPAZ MOUNTAIN GEM MINE—Site 30

Gem-quality topaz can be collected at this fee collecting location situated in the mountains a few miles north of Lake George. To get there from town, go west on Highway 24 toward Hartsel one and one-tenth miles, turn right onto County Road 77 and continue another six and seven-tenths miles. Turn right and drive another two and two-tenths miles to the parking area and check in at the office.

This is a placer deposit, and the topaz occurs among the reddish, decomposed granite gravels scattered throughout the claim. The mine operator removes the gem-bearing gravel with a tractor from where the topaz has settled near bedrock, about six to ten feet below the surface. It is then sifted through a coarse screen to eliminate large, worthless stones.

Collectors can choose between buckets or wheelbarrows of gem gravel. It is necessary to soak the gravel in water to soften the encasing clay. It is then placed on a screen and sprayed with a hose to remove the debris. Once cleaned, the topaz is easy to spot, since it glistens in the sunlight.

Most visitors find something worthwhile. Occasionally, a rockhound will find a real treasure, often of great value. Colors range through pale blue, pink and water-clear, with the blue and pink being the most prized. Sporadic bi-colored pieces can also be found, those being fairly valuable; and doubly terminated crystals, although generally small, can also be procured.

At time of publication, a fifty-pound bucket of screened gravel was available for $10, or three buckets for $25. Wheelbarrow loads were considerably higher in price. All equipment, including gloves, hose, screens, etc. are included in the price. You can also dig your own gravel from the pit, but you must supply your own digging equipment.

The Gem Mine is located high in the mountains, where the air is somewhat thin. For that reason, do not over extend yourself, especially if you choose to dig. It is, however, a most beautiful and restful place to spend some time, and the potential pay-off is limited only by how much time and effort you are willing to put forth. For more information, write Topaz Mountain Gem Mine, 2010 World Ave., Colorado Springs, Colorado 80909; or, during the summer write to Box 522, Lake George, Colorado 80827.

TOPAZ MOUNTAIN

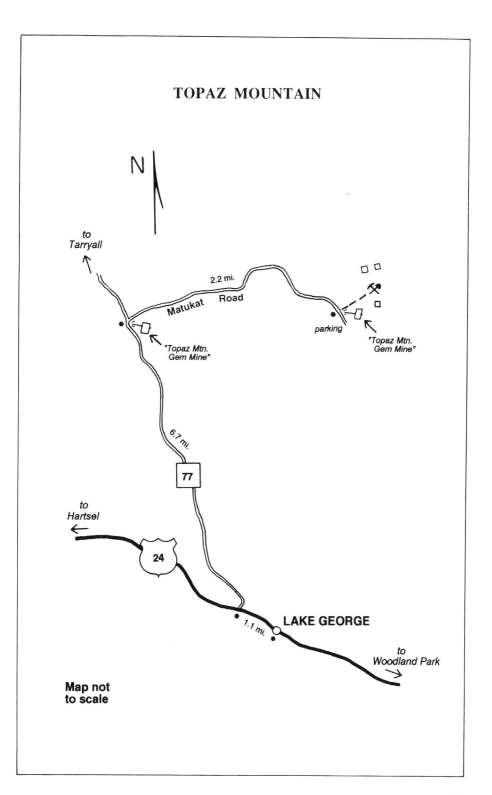

N

to
Tarryall

2.2 mi.

Matukat Road

"Topaz Mtn.
Gem Mine"

parking

"Topaz Mtn.
Gem Mine"

6.7 mi.

77

to
Hartsel

24

LAKE GEORGE

1.1 mi.

to
Woodland Park

Map not
to scale

Crystal Peak and Little Crystal Peak have gained fame throughout the world for producing some of the finest amazonite crystals available anywhere. Currently, both locations are surrounded by private land and are thereby inaccessible, unless permission can be obtained to cross through. These sites are mentioned because of their mineralogical importance and in the hopes that access might someday be provided, even if for a fee.

If you do get permission, trek to the base of the coarse pegmatite granite situated on the upper elevations. There is lots of graphic granite to be found, along with some nice feldspar, quartz and mica. The real prize is, of course, the beautiful, brilliant green and blue-green amazonite crystals. The amazonite is found in clay-filled cavities within the pegmatite granite or loose, in the lower slopes, having been weathered away from where they were formed. Needless to say, the finest specimens are those taken directly from the pockets, rather than from the rubble.

If you come upon a pocket in the host granite, be advised that the brilliantly colored crystals are sometimes difficult to identify, since they are usually coated with a thick clay. Dipping suspect crystals in water will quickly reveal their identity and quality. Be very careful when removing them from a cavity. Try to extract as large a portion of the wall as possible, since pieces containing multiple crystals are considerably more valuable than singles.

Beautiful black smoky quartz is often found in association with the amazonite, and pieces containing both of those minerals are extremely prized by collectors. The pegmatite granites of this region also boast green and purple fluorite, hematite, radiating balls of goethite and beautiful mica books. These minerals, too, can be found with the amazonite, providing the potential for extremely valuable specimens if carefully removed.

If you cannot get onto Crystal Peak or Little Crystal Peak, drive along any of the roads to the north within the national forest, and inspect some of the numerous pegmatite outcrops throughout the region. Although not as famous, these deposits do offer great potential, and many fine specimens have been found there.

Amazonite collected near Florissant

FLORISSANT CRYSTALS

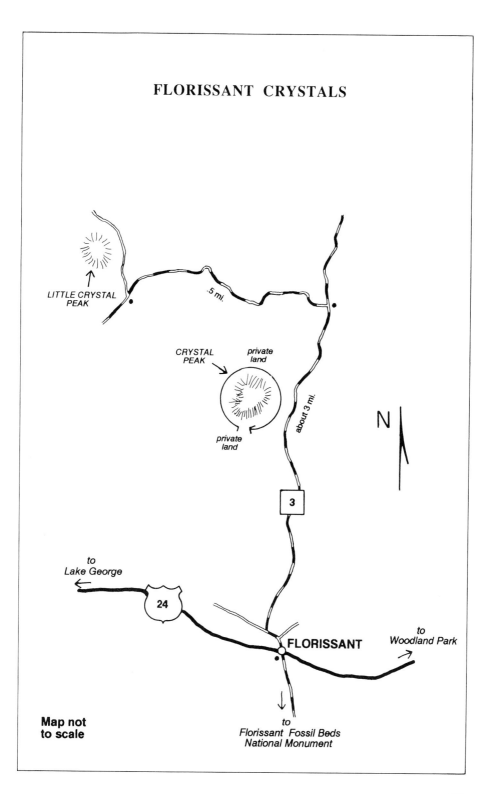

LITTLE CRYSTAL PEAK

.5 mi.

CRYSTAL PEAK

private land

private land

about 3 mi.

N

3

to Lake George

24

to Woodland Park

FLORISSANT

to Florissant Fossil Beds National Monument

Map not to scale

71

Remarkably well-preserved remnants of the various life forms that inhabited central Colorado over 35-million-years ago can be obtained just south of Florissant. The incredibly detailed leaves, plants and insects, as well as some of the largest petrified wood stumps in the world, occur in the grayish shales centered around the 6,000-acre Florissant Fossil Beds National Monument.

The Visitor's Center is two and two-tenths miles south of town and opened from 8:00 a.m. until 6:00 p.m. in the summer, and from 8:00 a.m. to 4:30 p.m. in the winter. Within the Monument, people can look at fossils, view informative exhibits on local geology and history and see informative charts and displays explaining how the fossils were originally formed.

Be advised that collecting within the Monument boundaries is NOT ALLOWED. For those who would like to have an opportunity to search for Florissant fossils, there is one place, the Nature's Wealth Fossil Shop, where it is possible to do so for a fee. The shop is located just three-tenths of a mile south of town, on the road to the Monument.

Collectors are allowed to split fossiliferous shale which has been removed by tractor from the hills surrounding the shop. At time of publication, the fee was $5.00 per person, per hour. The owner will assist, if necessary, but it will soon be up to you to sit down with a sharp knife and separate the thin layers in hopes of exposing the often tiny fossils. The shale splits easily, and it only takes time, patience and persistence for success.

Pieces containing lots of leaves and/or insects are the most valuable, and the black, carbonized fossils stand out nicely against the light gray shale, making them ideal for display. For those not lucky enough to find much, the rock shop has good specimens for sale.

More information can be obtained by writing to the Florissant Fossil Beds National Monument, P.O. Box 185, Florissant, Colorado 80816; or by contacting Nature's Wealth Fossil Shop, P.O. Box 5, Florissant, Colorado 80816.

Petrified tree stumps in the Florissant Fossil Beds National Monument

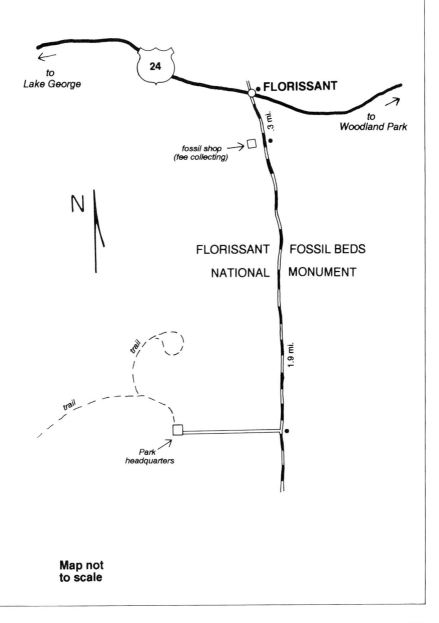

FLORISSANT FOSSILS

to
Lake George

24

● **FLORISSANT**

to
Woodland Park

.3 mi.

fossil shop →
(fee collecting)

N

FLORISSANT   FOSSIL BEDS

NATIONAL   MONUMENT

1.9 mi.

trail

trail

Park
headquarters

**Map not
to scale**

This location provides nice selenite crystals and occasional chunks of somewhat porous jasper. The Calhan Badlands also offer rockhounds an opportunity to explore a most fascinating geological occurrence. Long ago, the colorful clays that make up the unique mounds of the Badlands provided pigments for the local Indians, and the site is thereby also referred to as the Calhan Paint Mines.

It is situated on private property, as are so many of Colorado's collecting areas, but collectors are occasionally allowed in if permission is granted beforehand. Even if you do not gain permission to actually walk through this fascinating geological wonderland, a visit for photographs may still make the trek worthwhile.

To get there, go south on the Calhan Highway, which intersects Highway 24 on the east side of town. Proceed six-tenths of a mile to Paint Mine Road, where you should turn left and drive another two miles. At the given mileage, bear left at the fork onto East Paint Mine Road, and go another two-tenths of a mile to a locked gate in the fence on the left. You will see the unusual spires and pillars as you approach the turnoff.

Park in the pullout, just off the pavement, as shown on the map. If you have permission to enter the badlands, follow any of the trails leading down from the roadway.

The jasper tends to be littered just about anywhere, especially on the upper regions. As you explore those upper areas, watch out for the telltale orange and rust-red colors of the jasper, which stand out very well against the lighter soil.

The selenite is found on the mounds, hills, and spires, "growing" from the soft soil or in the low sandy regions. If you choose to search the sand, it is helpful to have a screen into which you can scoop the selenite-bearing soil. Please do not dig into the fragile spires and mounds, since no amount of jasper or selenite would be worth destroying this geologically fascinating locality.

*The unusual scenery
at Calhan Badlands*

CALHAN BADLANDS

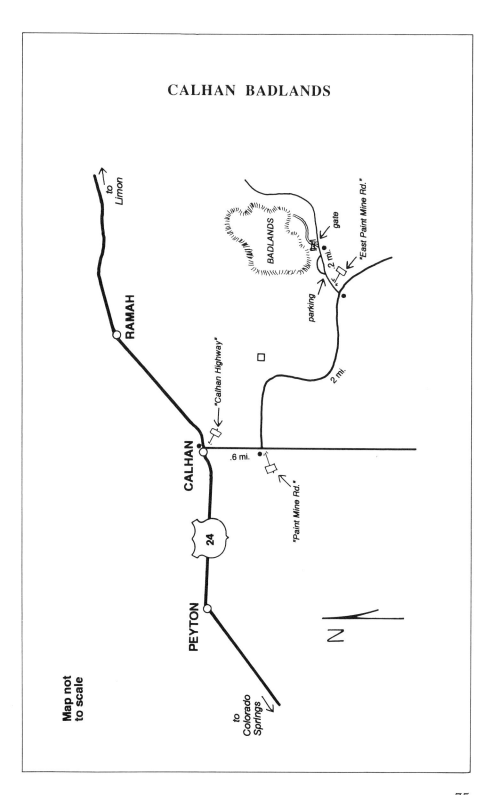

Map not
to scale

The region surrounding St. Peter's Dome, just west of Colorado Springs, has gained fame throughout the country for the fine specimens that have been gathered there. The list of gemstones having been found at this classic location is lengthy, and includes apatite, sphene, zircon, topaz, amazonite, and smoky quartz crystals. In addition, collectors have obtained water-clear quartz, pink feldspar, very large books of biotite mica, magnetite, and fluorite, as well as a host of other often valuable minerals.

As you travel along the road shown on the map, or any others in the region, numerous mine dumps will be encountered, and any of them afford great potential for supplying minerals and gemstones. Just be sure, before collecting, that you accurately ascertain whether or not the prospect is open to rockhounds.

It is generally helpful, when collecting on the dumps, to have a screen and shovel, in order to sift out the dirt and assist with sorting large rocks and crystals. A bucket of water could also be helpful, since some of the dump soil is quite fine and conceals the crystals true identity.

The trip starts where Highway 24 intersects 21st Street, just east of Colorado Springs. From there, head south on 21st Street, toward the zoo, four and six-tenths miles. The road changes names three times within that stretch, as shown on the map. At the given mileage, take the Old Stage Road as it winds its way up the steep mountain. Stay on the main road another seven and four-tenths miles to the shooting range turnoff. At that intersection is a parking area, and it is there where you can stop.

You will see a sign designating the trail leading to the summit of St. Peter's Dome and along that route are countless fine pegmatite outcrops and minerals as well as some spectacular views. Good specimens can be found just about anywhere on the slopes of St. Peter's Dome and other nearby peaks. Additional material is encountered by walking past the shooting range and examining the road cuts and surrounding terrain. The road is actually what is left of an old narrow gauge railroad bed, and it goes through at least three tunnels and affords some spectacular views.

Additional mine dumps will be encountered all the way to Cripple Creek, and, as was mentioned earlier, each affords great potential for supplying fine specimens. Just be sure to only collect on abandoned dumps.

It is difficult to say where you will have the best success. Good specimens can be obtained from just about any of the prospects in the region, as well as along the trail to and at the summit. Be sure to take water with you if you attempt the hike, and also carry a sturdy bag to hold specimens, rock pick, and a few chisels. Wherever you decide to explore in this most scenic region, do not hike farther than you can easily hike back from. This is high altitude and the trek back to your vehicle can be extremely difficult.

ST. PETER'S DOME

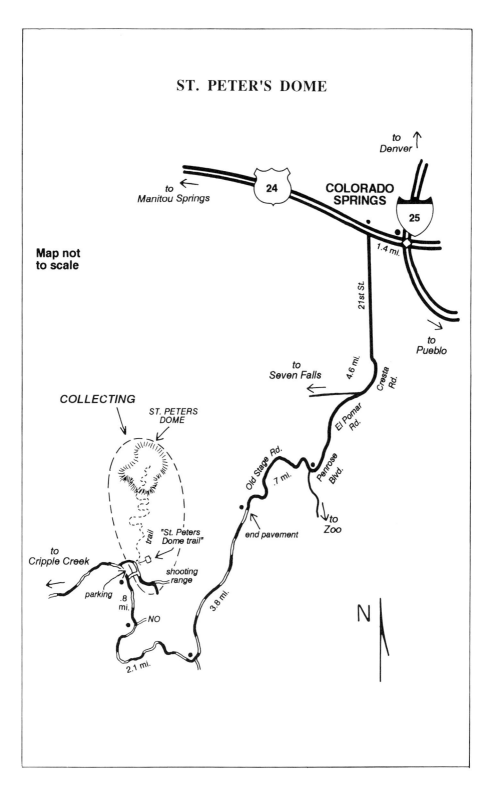

to
Denver

to
Manitou Springs

24

COLORADO
SPRINGS

25

1.4 mi.

21st St.

to
Pueblo

to
Seven Falls

4.6 mi.

Cresta
Rd.

El Pomar
Rd.

Map not
to scale

COLLECTING

ST. PETERS
DOME

Old Stage Rd.

.7 mi.

Penrose
Blvd.

to
Zoo

end pavement

"St. Peters
Dome trail"

trail

to
Cripple Creek

parking

.8
mi.

shooting
range

NO

3.8 mi.

N

2.1 mi.

Fossils and colorful jasper can be found throughout a somewhat extensive area about eleven miles south of Pueblo. To get there, take Exit 88 from Interstate 25 and go west. Approximately one-tenth of a mile from the interstate there is a road cut, on the south, exposing a layered, fossil-bearing occurrence of limestone. Park off the road and examine that deposit for traces of fossilized shells.

Break up the limestone with a sledge hammer and chisel in an effort to expose otherwise hidden fossils, and, in addition, carefully examine what has already been weathered loose. Sorting through the smaller pieces of limestone below the road cut is usually more productive than trying to remove it directly from the primary deposit. Be advised that nothing is overly plentiful here, but some of the specimens do make the effort worthwhile.

After having adequately explored the road cut, continue northwest, stopping from time to time, in order to conduct a quick survey. Large blocky chunks of limestone will be encountered, and such occurrences denote good places to explore. Carefully inspect all suspect limestone for partially exposed shells, keeping in mind that a chunk of host rock containing many fossils makes a far more interesting display piece than a single, solitary shell.

As you roam around, be also on the lookout for colorful jasper, which can be found randomly just about anywhere within the area. Some of it is porous and/or unappealing in color, but quality material is not too difficult to find. The best pieces tend to be small and primarily suitable only for tumbling.

After having traveled two and three-tenths miles, turn either left or right (it makes no difference). Continue at least one more mile in either direction,

stopping from time to time as you did before, hoping to find even more fossil-bearing limestone or colorful jasper.

It should be noted that there is another fossil-bearing limestone deposit on the eastern side of Interstate 25 at Exit 88, and that, too, should be looked at.

Fossil-bearing, limestone road cut by Exit 88

PUEBLO

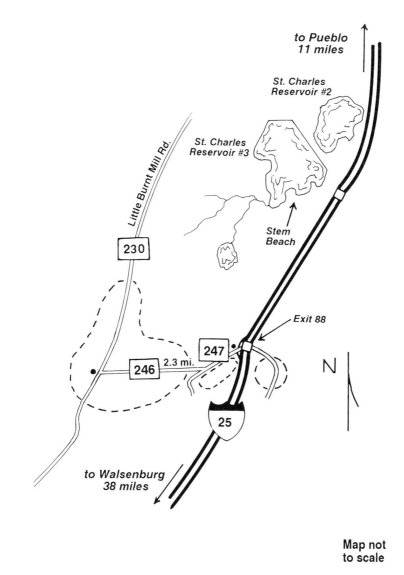

to Pueblo
11 miles

St. Charles
Reservoir #2

St. Charles
Reservoir #3

Little Burnt Mill Rd.

Stem
Beach

230

Exit 88

247

246 2.3 mi.

25

N

to Walsenburg
38 miles

**Map not
to scale**

This is an interesting location to visit, and affords the collector an opportunity to gather nice calcite specimens, some large enough to be cabinet pieces. Be advised, however, that most of what can be picked up here tends to be fist size or smaller.

To get to the site, start where Highway 115 intersects Highway 50, about twenty-seven miles west of Pueblo and just south of Penrose. Proceed south along Highway 115 one and three-tenths miles and park well off the road. There is a good place to pull off at the given mileage. When you do, be certain your vehicle does not protrude onto the highway, since it is on a curve, and vehicles often travel through here at high speeds.

Crawl under the highway fence and hike through the sandy valley, as illustrated on the map. The calcite can be found just about anywhere in the soft hills, on either side, extending for quite a distance. For some reason, however, I have had the best success by turning into the first little "canyon" on the left, about 100 yards from the pavement. Hike up the sandy draw and search for calcite "growing" from chunks of limestone.

Fairly good specimens can be found just lying about on the soft soil of the hills. If you want to obtain larger or less weathered materials, it is usually necessary to do some digging and splitting of the limestone. The digging is not difficult, since the soil is quite soft. It is advisable to first try to locate specimens on the surface, in order to get a good idea of what local material looks like. Lots of the surface material is weathered, but certainly not all of it. Do not toss out a promising piece until it has been thoroughly cleaned, since the fine sand tends to fill the spaces in the crystals and hide their true beauty.

As you walk throughout the area, be sure to keep your eyes to the ground, since the calcite is found randomly. For some reason, it seems to be concentrated in certain areas while little or nothing appears to be available at other spots, even though the terrain appears to be identical. Some of the calcite is stained a beautiful orange, and many of the crystals are terminated or in the form of near perfect rhombohedrons. Look for seams or cavities in chunks of the native limestone, since that is where the crystals originally formed. If carefully split, spectacular crystal-covered plates can be obtained. Such specimens are difficult to procure, however, since it requires a somewhat large chunk of limestone, a good, open, crystal-filled seam, and extremely careful splitting.

PENROSE CALCITE

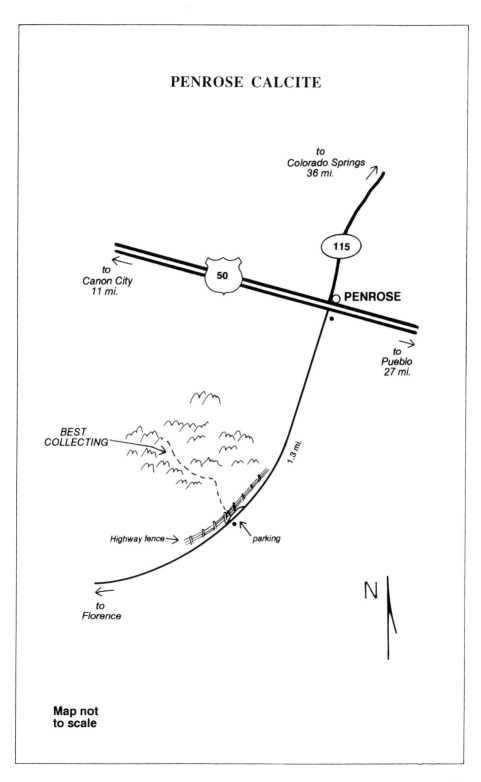

to
Colorado Springs
36 mi.

115

to
Canon City
11 mi.

50

○ PENROSE

to
Pueblo
27 mi.

BEST
COLLECTING

1.3 mi.

Highway fence→

parking

to
Florence

N

**Map not
to scale**

Dinosaur bone, jasper and nice orange marble can all be found in a somewhat condensed area north of Canon City. To get to this historic and fascinating region, go one block north on Raynolds Avenue, from where it intersects Highway 50, in Canon City. From there, turn left, continue another one-tenth of a mile, and then proceed north on Field Avenue five and seven-tenths miles, as illustrated on the accompanying map

At the given mileage, there is a road on the left going up a hill, which leads through Site B. All along that road, and scattered throughout the surrounding terrain, collectors can pick up nice pieces of quality pink and orange marble, most of which takes a good polish.

After having explored Site B, return to the main road and go two-tenths of a mile farther north. At that point, there is a turnout on the right and a small display discussing the geologic history of the area and marking the location where the Cleveland Museum made numerous significant paleontological discoveries. Occasional dinosaur bone fragments can be found on the opposite side of the river, as can nice agate and jasper, but getting across is difficult and unsafe, especially if the water level is high. Only cross the waterway if you are certain that it is safe to do so. Rather than risk an accident, it is better to continue up the road another two-tenths of a mile and park at the head of the canyon on the left.

Selenite, jasper, agate and jasperized dinosaur bone can also be found throughout that and other nearby canyons. Be advised, though, that the bone is not overly plentiful, since this is a world famous locality. Many people have visited over the years, and the surface has virtually been picked clean. The only bone that current collectors will be able to find is what has been recently exposed by rains, or a rare specimen that has been overlooked by others. Who knows, though, you might be lucky and spot the tip of a recently unearthed rib attached to a heretofore undiscovered dinosaur.

Parked near the site

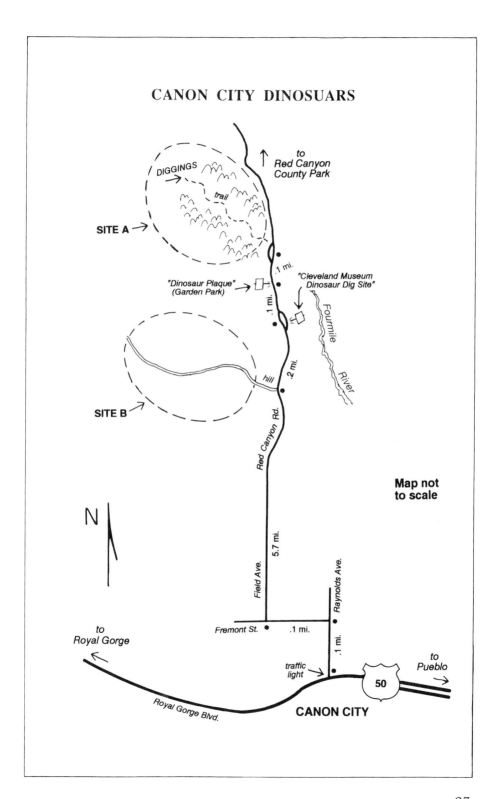

CANON CITY DINOSUARS

to
Red Canyon
County Park

DIGGINGS

trail

SITE A

"Dinosaur Plaque"
(Garden Park)

"Cleveland Museum
Dinosaur Dig Site"

1 mi.

.1 mi.

Fourmile
River

SITE B

hill

.2 mi.

Red Canyon Rd.

Map not
to scale

N

5.7 mi.

Field Ave.

Raynolds Ave.

Fremont St.   .1 mi.

.1 mi.

to
Royal Gorge

traffic
light

to
Pueblo

50

Royal Gorge Blvd.   CANON CITY

Lots of pegmatite mineral specimens can be gathered just north of the famous Royal Gorge. To get to the center of this somewhat widespread site, turn south from Highway 50 onto Royal Gorge Road and proceed two and two-tenths miles. At that point, there is a large sign designating a right turn to Buckskin Joe, but you, instead, should go left onto the dirt road.

Immediately after turning off the pavement, you will see pegmatite minerals scattered in all directions for quite a distance. Beautiful orange and pink feldspar, as well as mica, often occurring in sizable and well-compacted books, can be picked up by walking only a short distance from your vehicle, wherever you choose to stop. In fact, the mica is so prevalent that the sun causes it to glisten, making the road and all of the surrounding terrain sparkle as you drive along.

It isn't necessary to go very far to obtain worthwhile specimens. Pull off at any random spot and roam the countryside searching for the best the location has to offer. Breaking up some of the larger boulders might prove fruitful, if you can't find anything of interest in the tons of more readily available smaller chunks.

There are a few mines which can be seen on the hillsides as you proceed down the road. They are all currently protected by valid claims and collecting is restricted. The owners of the rock shop situated just south of Buckskin Joe oversee many of them, however, and arrangements to visit one or more of them might be possible by inquiring. It really doesn't make any difference, however, since what can be found along the road and surrounding regions, is as good as that which can be obtained on any of the dumps.

Good specimens of local minerals can be found at any of the local rock shops. Since it is always a good idea to know exactly what you are looking for before collecting, a short stop at any or all of them may prove to be useful.

Examining a pegmatite

ROYAL GORGE

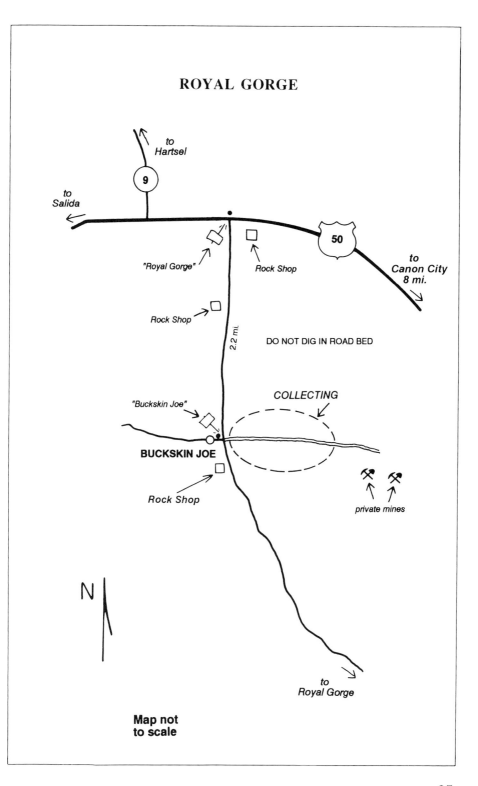

A good selection of pegmatite minerals can be procured on the dumps of the once productive Border Feldspar Mine, situated just north of the famous Royal Gorge.

To get there, turn south from Highway 50 onto Royal Gorge Road and proceed two and two-tenths miles. At that point, there will be a large sign designating a right turn to Buckskin Joe, but you should continue straight ahead another four-tenths of a mile. Immediately after passing the Royal Gorge Park sign, there is a turnout on the right with large boulders of mica-filled feldspar blocking access to the mine road.

You must park at those boulders and hike about fifty yards to the abandoned quarry. The trek is very easy, and the old road is littered with fine mineral specimens.

At the mine itself, dig through the dumps to find the best the location has to offer. Of primary interest is the beautiful pink and orange feldspar, much of which displays nice crystal faces and often occurs in association with clean mica books. Black tourmaline can also be found, usually associated with other minerals, and such specimens are frequently suitable for display in mineral collections.

The Border Feldspar Mine has been abandoned for quite a few years, but there is no guarantee that this will always be the situation. As is the case when collecting at any mine, be sure to accurately ascertain whether or not rockhounds are allowed in at the time of your visit. If unsure, inquire at any of the nearby rock shops. Good samples of local minerals can be found at any of them, and a short stop at one of the nearby rock shops may prove to be quite helpful, since it is always a good idea to know exactly what to look for before collecting.

BORDER FELDSPAR MINE

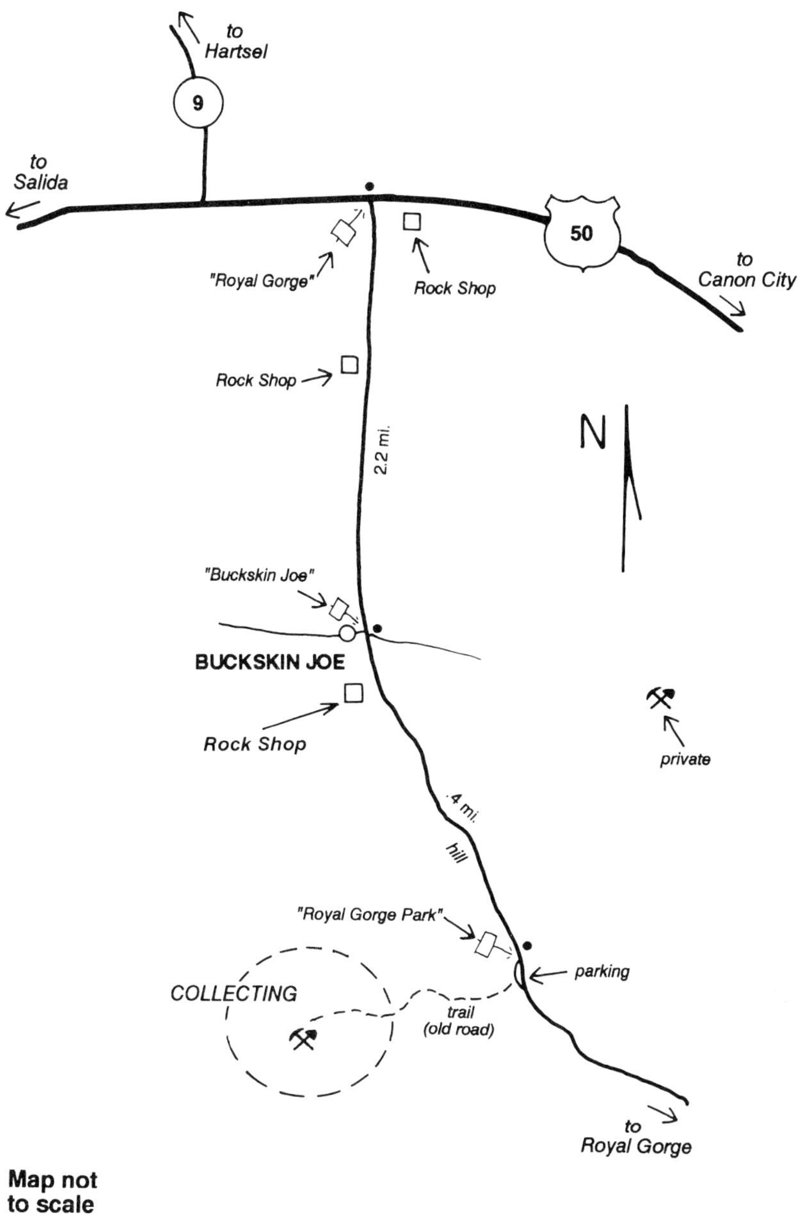

to
Hartsel

9

to
Salida

50

to
Canon City

"Royal Gorge"

Rock Shop

Rock Shop

2.2 mi.

N

"Buckskin Joe"

BUCKSKIN JOE

Rock Shop

private

.4 mi.

hill

"Royal Gorge Park"

parking

COLLECTING

trail
(old road)

to
Royal Gorge

**Map not
to scale**

Pegmatite minerals and some of the finest rose quartz available in Colorado can be found at two sites situated in the rugged hills north of Texas Creek. These are not easy locations to get to and four-wheel drive is highly recommended. To get to the sites, head north on the road which intersects Highway 50 just west of the Texas Creek Store. You will cross the Arkansas River after going one-tenth of a mile and railroad tracks will be encountered another two-tenths of a mile along the way. Cross the cattle guard and go right into the large wash.

Proceed through the sandy arroyo until you have gone two miles from the cattle guard and then turn left onto the road leading up the hillside. This is Table Mountain Road and is designated as Road 5029 on one sign and, a short distance farther along, Road 6055. Follow it as it leads across a flat mesa and then drops into a narrow little canyon, about two miles from where it exited the wash. It is in and around that canyon where you will find the pink feldspar and mica. It is difficult to turn around in the narrow canyon, making it necessary to go about one-half mile farther to maneuver around.

To reach Site A, return to the large wash, continue north another six-tenths of a mile to where tracks lead out of the sand, on the right. From there the road isn't too bad as it switchbacks up the steep mountain another one and six-tenths miles to the summit. Just past the summit the rose quartz mine, with its pink dumps, can be spotted on the opposite mountain. Continue one mile, down the hill, past the mine road, to a turnout on the left. Park off the road and hike to the bottom of the main dump.

This mine has been worked periodically over the years. If it is not abandoned, restrict collecting to the lowlands, washes, and other unclaimed regions, since plenty can be found in those locations. Inquiry regarding collecting status at the Texas Creek Trading Post would be wise before making the rugged trip. The dumps contain boulders of richly colored rose quartz as well as a host of other pegmatite minerals, including biotite mica, tourmaline, vividly colored pink and orange feldspar and crystal clear quartz.

Site A

TEXAS CREEK ROSE QUARTZ

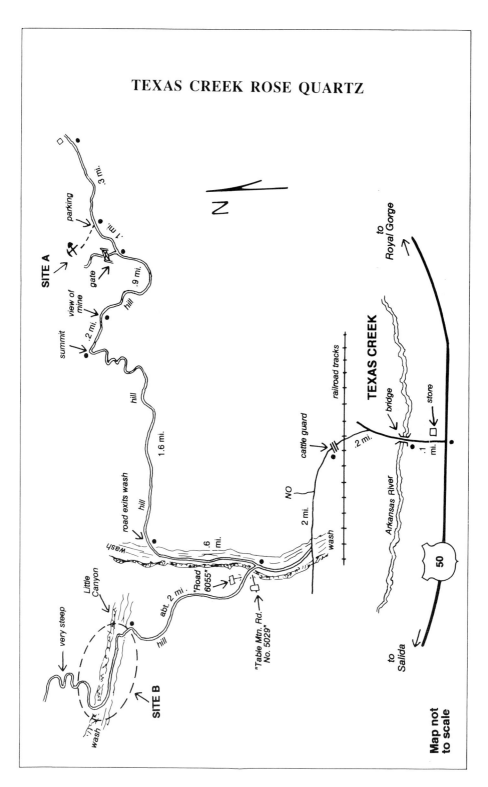

Map not
to scale

89

A wide range of fossils and some tiny calcite crystals can be obtained just west of La Veta Pass, about thirteen miles east of Fort Garland. To get there, take Highway 160 seven miles west from La Veta Pass and pull completely off the pavement near the large road cut to the north. If you get to an unusual, dome topped building, as illustrated on the map, you have gone too far and should double back exactly one mile to the western edge of this interesting collecting site.

The road cut at the given mileage, and others continuing at least two more miles to the east, are all composed of gray, fossil-bearing shale. Encased within the layers of shale, collectors can find, among other things, small samples of fossilized coral, tiny sea shells, and small sea snails. In addition, some pieces have been filled with often beautifully crystallized crusts of calcite. Look for obvious white regions between layers to designate the possibility of calcite inclusion.

The best way to explore this area is to examine what has already been broken loose from the primary deposit by sorting through the rubble at the base of the road cuts. Just take a chink of the shale and split it with a gentle tap of a hammer onto a small chisel or knife inserted within a bedding plane. After splitting, carefully examine the freshly exposed surface for fossils and/or calcite crystals

Be sure to allow sufficient time to explore more than one of the numerous road cuts cutting through the shale. Climbing onto the road cuts can be very hazardous and is not recommended. The shale is crumbly and thereby unstable. Do not knock any rock onto the roadway, since it could be hazardous to traffic, and, in addition, be extremely careful crossing the highway, especially if you have children along. Vehicles drive this stretch of curvy pavement at high speeds and are not expecting to see someone crossing.

Fossil-bearing shale in the road cut

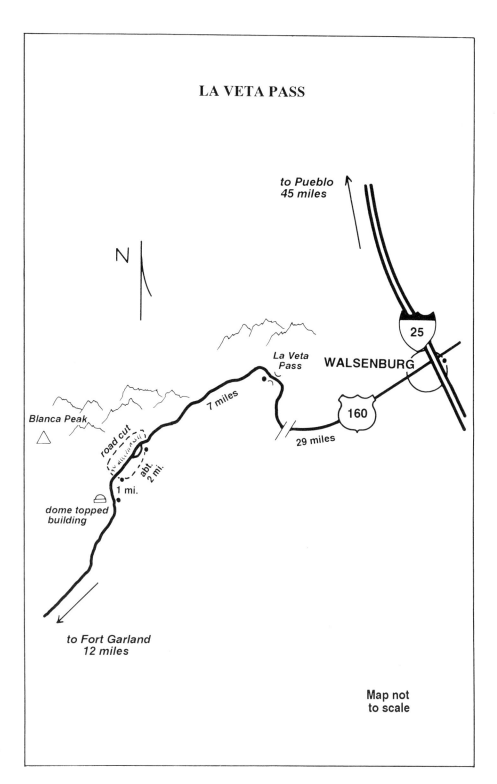

LA VETA PASS

to Pueblo 45 miles

N

La Veta Pass

WALSENBURG

25

7 miles

160

29 miles

Blanca Peak

road cut

abt. 2 mi.

1 mi.

dome topped building

to Fort Garland 12 miles

Map not to scale

91

This location offers rockhounds lots of little calcite crystals, both terminated and rhombohedral, but accessibility is intermittent, since it lies on the U.S. Army Pinon Canyon Maneuver Site. A visitor's pass can usually be obtained at the headquarters, located at 36086 U.S. Highway 350. Permission to enter the facility MUST be secured in advance. Occasionally, passes will be supplied on the day of the visit, but it is strongly recommended to attempt getting that permission well ahead of time. This is a remote spot and it would not be enjoyable to drive such a distance only to be told that the military is conducting maneuvers, thereby closing the entire region.

After securing permission to enter the Military Reservation, take Highway 350 to the small town of Model. From the gas station, go northeast six-tenths of a mile to Road 540, and turn right. Proceed five and eight-tenths miles on the well-maintained road to a fork. The left fork leads to the Military Reservation, and a locked gate is there to greet you. Arrangements to have the gate opened are made when the visitor's pass is issued. Once through the gate, continue one and two-tenths miles, bearing right toward the little hills.

The calcite crystals will be found "growing" in cavities and veins throughout the easily-spotted shale and limestone layers. The cavities are fairly easy to locate, since they are usually lined with an easily spotted, greenish calcite. The interiors often contain excellent and frequently water-clear Iceland spar, as well as nice, but small, terminated crystals. Breaking into the cavities does take some perseverance and lots of hard work with sledge hammer, chisels and gads, but much of what can be found is of very high quality, making the labor worthwhile.

The limestone in this region also contains fossils, primarily in the form of shells, including some interesting ammonites. While here, be sure to also explore those possibilities.

TRINIDAD CALCITE

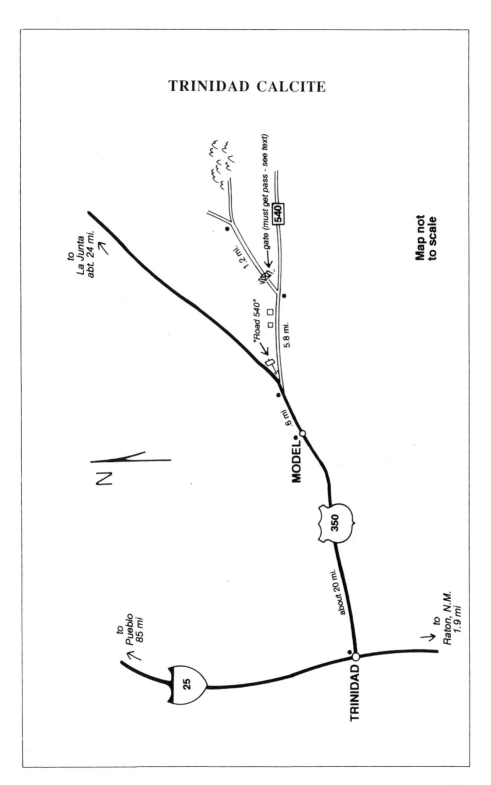

Map not to scale

93

This location is extensive, and, within its boundaries, rockhounds can find lots of colorful agate, jasper, chalcedony, barite and alabaster, and, also, be treated to some of Colorado's most spectacular scenery.

The journey begins in the town of Whitewater, about fifteen miles southeast of Grand Junction. From there, proceed onto Highway 141 toward Naturita. Starting only a few miles from Whitewater, and continuing all the way to Naturita, the streams and washes afford collectors lots of fine agate, jasper and other colorful cutting materials. The procedure for collecting in this region is to stop from time to time as you drive southward.

Be sure to park well off the pavement when collecting here, since, in places, the road is quite narrow, and other drivers are not expecting to encounter a parked car on the highway.

When you reach Gateway, about forty-four miles from Whitewater, go another four miles, as illustrated on the map, to where a hill will be seen adjacent to the pavement on the west. About one-tenth of a mile past that hill is a good place to pull off. Hike back and crawl under the highway fence to what remains of an old barite mine. Be advised that from the road this doesn't look at all like a mine. It appears to be a dirt hill next to the pavement. Much of the rock in the soft soil is barite and, when thoroughly washed, often displays nice tabular crystals. The least weathered specimens are obtained by either digging with a trowel in the soil or attempting to remove chunks with hard rock from seams encased in the native red sandstone.

About one and one-half miles farther along the highway is an alabaster mine. This site was CLOSED at the time of the author's last visit. A few specimens can be picked up outside the mine gate. The light colored alabaster seam can be seen extending along the cliffs for quite a distance back toward Gateway. Access to portions of that seam, which are not on the claim, might be possible from the barite spot, if you are interested.

Scenery on the way to the collecting area

GATEWAY

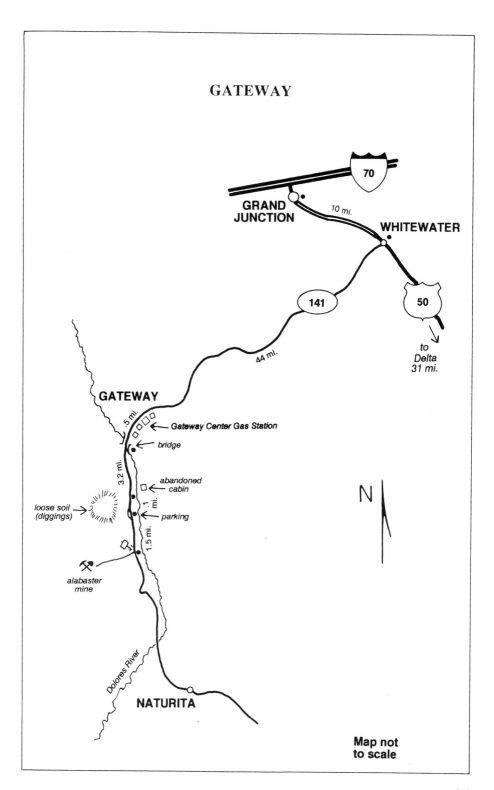

Hammers

Probably the one piece of equipment most identified with rockhounding and prospecting is the hand-held rock pick. Generally, one side of the head is blunt and flat, while the opposite is either pointed or chisel shaped. If there is only one tool you can take on a field trip, this surely would be the most useful for most situations. The flattened end is handy for cracking small rocks and driving chisels or gads into seams or cracks. The pointed or flattened end is good for light digging or for prying open cracks.

A sledge hammer is extremely helpful if you need to break up sizable pieces of rock or are trying to extract gems still encased in seams or cavities. A sledge hammer also supplies more power for pounding chisels or gads into hard rock, or for breaking off samples from an outcrop. Sledge hammers come in a variety of weights and are available with short or long handles.

Rock Chisels, Gads, and Star Drills

A rock chisel is a hand tool, with a sharpened flat end, used to trim specimens, chip off samples, or to split rocks and seams. A gad is a similar hand tool, but, instead of having a flat end, it is pointed. Gads are primarily used to break up rock or are inserted in cracks or seams to split them open.

Gads are more useful to rockhounds, since their pointed and tapered ends tend to get farther inside cracks and crevices than chisels. A star drill looks much like a gad, but it is thinner and primarily used to make holes in rock within which a gad can be inserted to do its job.

Gads, chisels, and star drills can be purchased in a variety of widths, lengths and weights. As is the case with hammers, be certain to obtain only those designed for use on rock.

Trowel

A trowel is a small hand-held digging tool which is very helpful when exploring mine dumps, washes, or regions where light digging of soft surface soil is required.

Pry Bar

Pry bars often come in handy when working hard rock seams or cavities. Furthermore, they can be used to break up tough soil and move large boulders. Pry bars afford better leverage than smaller hand tools and are much stronger, thereby being less likely to bend or break.

Pick and Shovel

Picks and shovels are needed when you must dig to locate minerals. At many sites, the surface material has all been taken, but, not too far below, there are still lots of excellent specimens. Getting to those otherwise hidden stones is made possible by using a pick and shovel.

Amazonite crystals from the region north of Florissant

Smoky quartz crystals found at Devil's Head

Specimen containing feldspar, quartz, pyrite, galena and sphalerite from a mine near Ouray

97

Blue barite — Stoneham area

Black tourmaline in quartz

Galena from a mine near Creede

*Mica and feldspar specimen
collected in the Royal Gorge area*

Common opal from Opal Hill

Cross section of dinosaur bone

Apache tears still embedded in host rock

Mica & quartz boulder—Wilkerson Pass

Chalcedony from Piñon Mesa

Lepidolite, mica, tourmaline, and quartz — Parlin

Garnet crystal in native rock from the Nathrop area

Barite collected at Gateway

Fluorite found at a mine near Silverton

Nodules which may contain calcite

Broken nodule showing calcite and barite

101

Quartz and mica — Texas Creek

Interesting group of feldspar crystals

*Specimen of mica, quartz
and feldspar collected
at Golden Gate*

*A seam of barite in a boulder
discovered near Gateway*

*Amazonite crystals found near
St. Peter's Dome*

102

A small geode from the Saguache collecting location

Small feldspar crystals from the
Trout Creek region

An especially nice sample of Barite
found near Hartsel

Mica and quartz collected from the Nederland area

Pyrite from Leadville

Rhodocrosite specimen found at the Alma collecting site

A round ended shovel is the best for digging, while the most efficient pick is a mattock. One side of a mattock's digging end is pointed and the opposite side is flat and chisel-like. A mattock pick is capable of doing all kinds of digging, from precise trenching to large scale dirt moving. The pointed end offers excellent penetration, especially if working in hard soil, and, once the soil is loosened, the chisel end is great for removing dirt quickly.

Safety Goggles

Safety goggles are a must when doing any hammering onto hard rock. Rock fragments or splintered metal from your hammer can fly off at the speed of a bullet when struck, thereby creating a potentially hazardous situation.

Hat and Proper Clothing

Taking clothing appropriate to the location(s) you will be visiting is essential if you want the trip to be an enjoyable experience. Be prepared for just about anything. Rain, mud, extremely hot weather, extremely cold weather, and even insects. Do some research on the region you plan to visit. Will you be in the barren and desolate desert or rugged mountains? Should you expect snow or rain, or will it be scorching hot?

Footwear is also of prime importance. Wear shoes appropriate to the terrain you will be exploring. If going to wet areas, waterproof shoes would be nice, as would an extra dry pair. If in hot and arid regions, shoes that "breathe" should be considered.

Gloves

If you plan to do anything except pick up specimens from the surface, gloves are recommended. Using a rock pick or sledge hammer for a few hours, or digging with pick and shovel, can cause painful blisters, cuts, and abrasions on one's hands. The associated tenderness and pain can quickly take the joy out of a collecting expedition. A good pair of gloves can make such handicaps less likely.

Collecting Bag or Backpack

When you visit a collecting site, it will probably be necessary to do some walking from where you park, and it is surprising how far you might stray. There is a limit to how much a person can carry in their pockets and hands, however, and that limit seems to always be reached just before coming upon the most beautiful specimen of your hike. A sturdy bag or backpack made from canvas or rip-stop nylon comes in quite handy in situations like this.

From *The Rockhound's Handbook* by James R. Mitchell

The two locations described here provide collectors with crystal-filled geodes, agate, feldspar, mica, amethyst, and chalcedony. To get to the first, labeled Site A on the accompanying map, go south ten miles from Grand Junction, on Highway 50, to Whitewater. From there, continue toward Delta approximately two more miles to the start of this extensive collecting area.

At the given mileage, you will notice some grayish cliffs to the east, and they continue south for at least another ten miles. Just about anywhere along that ten mile stretch one can find crystallized, calcite-filled geodes. The major problem with this location is gaining access. There are very few safe places to pull off the pavement, and, in addition, it is difficult to get through the highway fence. There are a few such spots, though, but you might have to double back a few times to find them. Don't pull off the pavement in places you might get stuck, and, under no circumstances, leave any portion of your vehicle protruding onto the highway. One fairly good access is about three and one-half miles south of Whitewater, as illustrated on the map. At that point, there is not only a small turnout, but also a gate through the fence.

From wherever you decide to access the gray, concretion-bearing ridge of shale, simply hike to its base and examine the rubble down below. It won't take long to find pieces of geodes, some of which are very nice, but patience is required to gather complete orbs. The least hazardous method of collecting is to restrict your search to the lowlands, paralleling the base of the cliffs for as long as you desire. If, however, you want to increase the chance for finding complete and less damaged specimens, scramble to the darker, geode-filled bands within the gray shale. Digging in those areas will greatly enhance your degree of success.

To get to Site B, return to Whitewater and go left onto Highway 141. Continue eleven and two-tenths miles and pull off, on the right, onto the small clearing just past the little bridge. This region is noted for the fine amethyst that is being mined nearby, but those primary sources are off limits to collectors. Rockhounds can, however, find a good selection of minerals by hiking along the creek or examining rubble below the mines. Beautiful feldspar crystals, agate, chalcedony, mica, garnet and even some occasional amethyst are encountered here. It won't take long to gather a good quantity of fine specimens.

Do not collect on any mine dumps unless you are certain it is allowed. The major active mines are well posted and those signs should be respected.

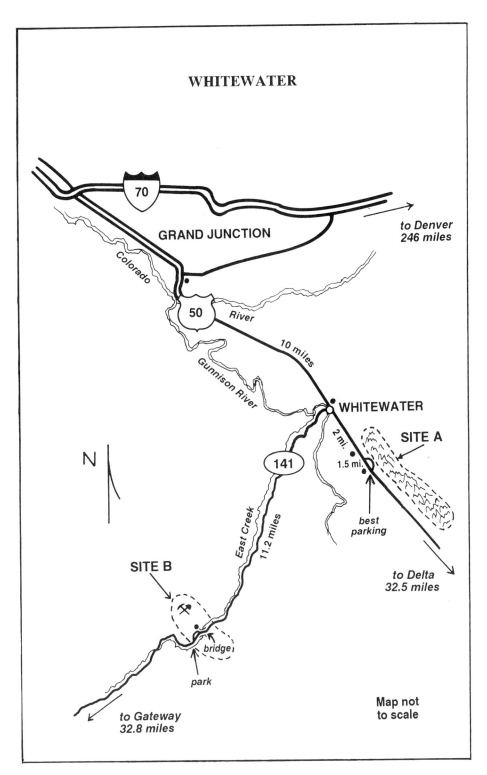

WHITEWATER

70

GRAND JUNCTION

to Denver
246 miles

Colorado

50

River

10 miles

Gunnison River

WHITEWATER

2 mi.

SITE A

141

1.5 mi.

best
parking

East Creek

11.2 miles

to Delta
32.5 miles

SITE B

N

bridge

park

to Gateway
32.8 miles

Map not
to scale

Good quality agate, chalcedony, petrified wood and jasper can be gathered among the pine trees south of Glade Park. The collecting occurs on Piñon Mesa, and most vehicles can easily make the trip. To get there from the Glade Park Store, go south on 16.5 S. Road three and one-half miles to where it begins ascending the mesa. At the given mileage, and extending for nearly twenty more miles, just about anywhere you choose to stop offers possible specimens.

Lots of bubbly chalcedony can be picked up, as well as a variety of agate, including some with exceptionally nice moss and dendritic inclusions. The petrified wood is usually not acceptable for polishing, but it can frequently be used for display in mineral collections. It tends to be somewhat grainy, but shows original wood structure very well. In addition, some of the wood contains small crystal-filled cavities which are very showy.

There are a number of ways to collect here, the simplest being to drive along the main, graded, dirt road, as it winds its way across Piñon Mesa, stopping from time to time to sample what is available. Pay particularly close attention to clearings and regions of erosion, where the material is more easily spotted. Searching terrain buried under pine needles is somewhat futile, unless you are willing to do lots of raking.

If you have a rugged vehicle, exploring some of the side roads, either leading off the main road across the mesa or accessing from different locations, can also be very productive. As is the case at all rockhounding sites, the most easily accessible areas usually provide more sparse collecting, while regions that are tougher to get to afford far greater opportunities. If you can travel on rough roads, follow any of the countless ruts, and, after driving a short distance, stop to see what you can find. If not satisfied, continue on a little farther and try again. You can spend days examining this pleasant, tree-covered locality. Be patient and have a willingness to spend some time and you will certainly be able to gather lots of fine specimens.

View of the surrounding area

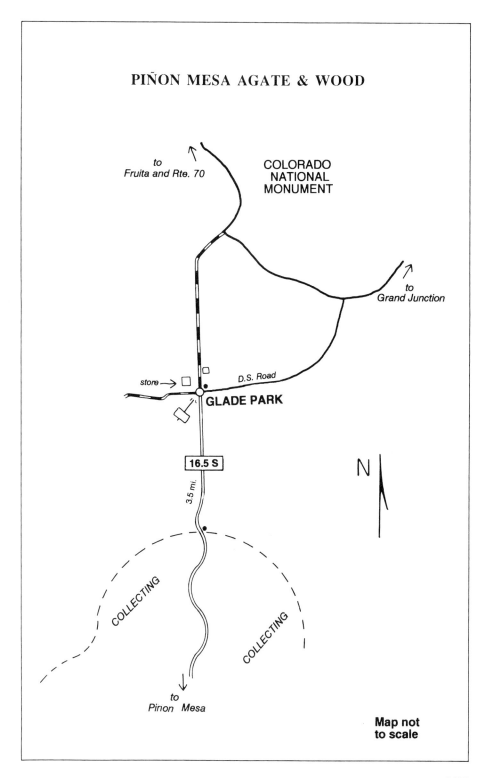

PIÑON MESA AGATE & WOOD

to
Fruita and Rte. 70

COLORADO
NATIONAL
MONUMENT

to
Grand Junction

store →

D.S. Road

GLADE PARK

16.5 S

3.5 mi.

N

COLLECTING

COLLECTING

to
Pinon Mesa

Map not
to scale

Excellent specimens of pink feldspar, frequently exhibiting well-formed crystal faces, as well as mica, nice jasper and brilliant white quartz, can be picked up at these two sites. To get to Site A, take Highway 24 two and four-tenths miles south from Buena Vista to where it joins Highway 24. From there, go east on Highway 24/285 six and one-tenth miles to the Trout City Inn, and turn right, just past the buildings. Follow the graded dirt road as it curves back to the east for one and nine-tenths miles. If you get to County Road 308, double back one-tenth of a mile and park.

As you make your way to the excavations, keep your eyes out for colorful jasper. It can be found just about anywhere, but it isn't overly plentiful. The flatlands, below the hill, as well as higher regions, all offer potential. I have had best luck down below, roaming the flats between the road and the hill. The quartz and the best of the feldspar are obtained in and around the old quarry. Either dig in the dumps or inspect the tons of loose debris. Additional specimens can be gathered above the mine from unexcavated pegmatite outcrops or scattered throughout the hillside below.

Some of the feldspar is a beautiful pink and orange, and, if in association with brilliant white quartz, is excellent for display in a mineral collection. Look for pieces with the feldspar showing good crystal faces. There is so much available, that collectors must allow sufficient time to sort and trim only the best the location has to offer.

Site B is reached by returning to the intersection of Highways 24 and 285, and proceeding south on Highway 285 for twelve and one-half miles to County Road 194. There is a sign at the intersection designating this to be the road to Brown Canyon. Follow County Road 194 for about one mile to where some massive mine dumps will be encountered. From there and continuing for at least another few miles, additional mines will be spotted throughout the surrounding area, all offering some potential for finding nice specimens of fluorite, feldspar, and mica.

These mines (Site A and Site B) have been abandoned for quite a long time, but, as is the case with any mine, that status is subject to change. Do not trespass on any that appear to once again be operating.

Old abandoned quarry near Buena Vista

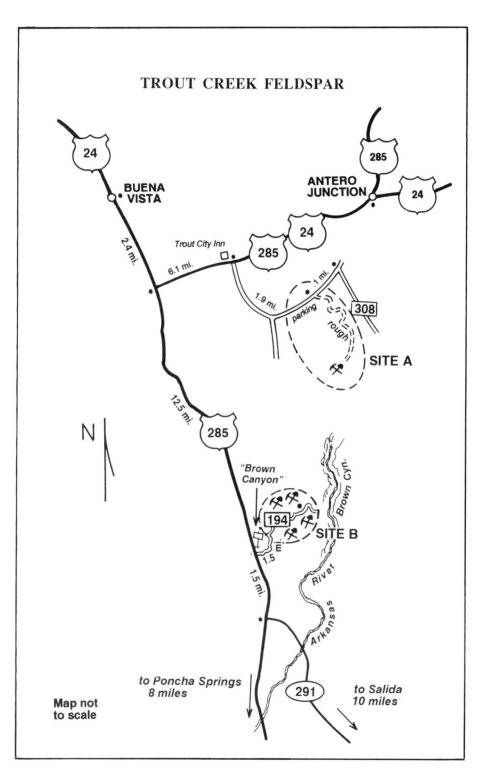

TROUT CREEK FELDSPAR

24

BUENA
VISTA

285

ANTERO
JUNCTION

24

24

Trout City Inn

285

2.4 mi.

6.1 mi.

1.9 mi.

.1 mi.

parking

308

rough

SITE A

N

12.5 mi.

285

"Brown
Canyon"

194

Brown Cyn.

SITE B

1.5 mi.

River

1.5 mi.

Arkansas

to Poncha Springs
8 miles

291

to Salida
10 miles

Map not
to scale

Excellent garnet crystals, yellow topaz, and tiny Apache tears can be gathered from Sugarloaf Mountain and Ruby Mountain, a short distance east of Nathrop. To get to Ruby Mountain, go north from the post office, on Highway 285, one and eight-tenths miles. From there, turn right, proceed two-tenths of a mile to the bridge over the Arkansas River, and drive another four-tenths of a mile to a sign designating the turnoff to Ruby Mountain. Follow that graded dirt road two and three-tenths more miles, and then bear left at the sign marking the end of County Road 300. From that point, it gets a little rougher, but most rugged vehicles should have no problem continuing, if driven carefully and it isn't muddy.

After going only one-tenth of a mile farther, park, and prepare to hike a short distance. There is a faint trail switching up the mountain, and it should be followed to the abandoned perlite mine. At that point, the ground is littered with countless black Apache tears, and it doesn't take long to gather hundreds of the tiny gemstones, some of which are clear enough to facet.

The famous Nathrop garnet crystals, and more rare yellow topaz, are found lining cavities within the rhyolite regions, which can be easily seen from down below. It takes some patience to expose the elusive crystals, and hard rock tools are needed to break out portions of the tough rhyolite in an effort to expose the precious garnets. This is difficult and time-consuming work, but it is often well rewarded since many of the gems can be quite sizable and extremely clean.

After Ruby Mountain, be sure to either hike or drive as close as you can to Sugarloaf Mountain. It may not have been thoroughly explored, due to its slightly less convenient location, but that only enhances its desirability. Look for garnet-bearing cavities in the rhyolite, as you did on Ruby Mountain.

As an extra bonus, there is lots of nice feldspar and mica available throughout the region, and the view of the Arkansas River and surrounding countryside is spectacular from either peak.

Ruby Mountain, a short distance east of Nathrop

NATHROP GEMS

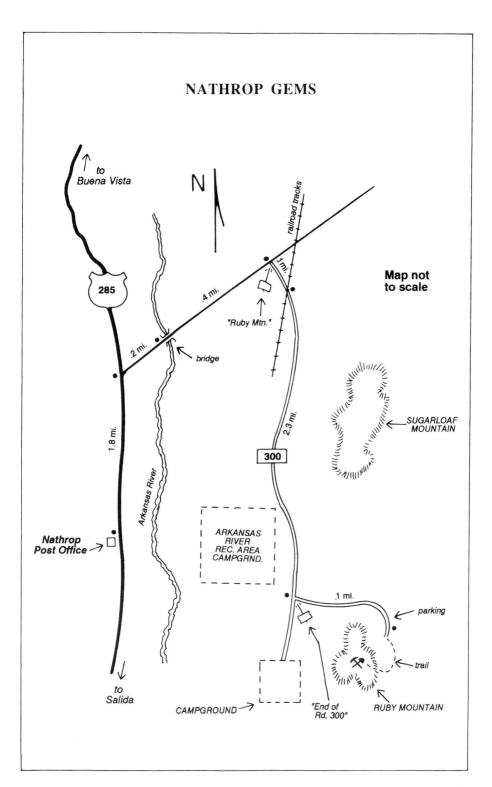

to
Buena Vista

N

railroad tracks

285

.4 mi.

.1 mi.

"Ruby Mtn."

Map not
to scale

.2 mi.

bridge

2.3 mi.

SUGARLOAF
MOUNTAIN

300

1.8 mi.

ARKANSAS
RIVER
REC. AREA
CAMPGRND.

.1 mi.

parking

Nathrop
Post Office →

Arkansas River

trail

RUBY MOUNTAIN

to
Salida

CAMPGROUND →

"End of
Rd. 300"

This is one of Colorado's most renowned gemstone collecting locations, boasting crystal clear aquamarine, beautiful smoky quartz, fluorite and topaz, as well as a host of other lesser minerals. It must be strongly emphasized, however, that the road to the site is EXTREMELY rough and precarious, as it switchbacks up to the summit of massive Mt. Antero. The trip MUST be taken in a high-clearance, four-wheel drive unit and attempted only by those with great experience in driving extremely rugged, rocky roads.

To get to Mt. Antero Summit Road, start in Nathrop, just south of the post office. Turn west onto well-graded County Road 162, and, after having gone four and two-tenths miles, Mt. Princeton Hot Springs will be encountered. Seven and seven-tenths miles farther along is the Antero Road. Just as you head up the hill, there is a warning to travelers of the extreme roughness ahead and its inherent dangers. Heed those warnings!

The summit is encountered about seven miles after leaving County Road 162, and you will be able to see where previous collectors have pulled out for parking and turning around. The gems are found in pockets within the bright white Antero granite, which is easily identified. Anywhere you see the telltale granite, either in its place on the mountain or in rubble farther below, there is potential for locating gemstones. You can start inspecting the granite at just about any place it is encountered, primarily near road's end at Antero Summit, within the saddle between Mt. Antero and Mt. White and near the top of Mt. White.

The brilliant blue aquamarines are the most ardently sought gemstones from the Mt. Antero region, but exquisite phenakite, bertrandite, beryl, crystal clear quartz, green and purple fluorite, spectacular and often sizable smoky

quartz crystals, topaz, mica, goethite, garnet, apatite, tourmaline, and a host of other highly-prized minerals and gemstones have also been reported emanating from this most productive area.

Road leading up to Mt. Antero Summit

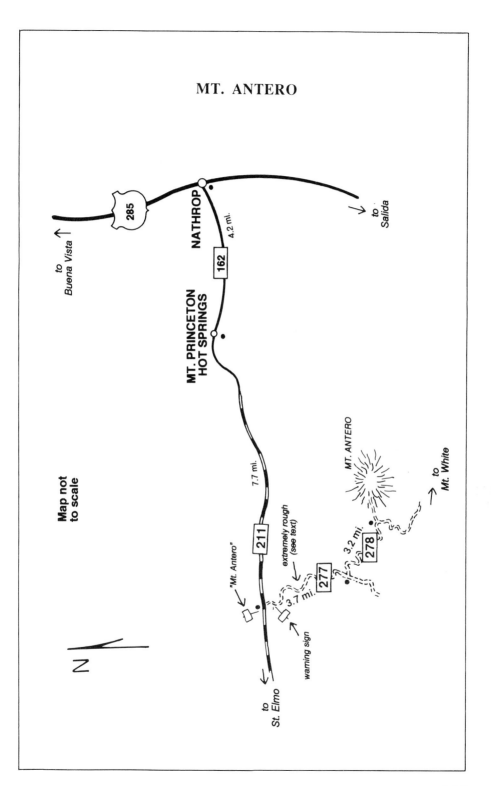

MT. ANTERO

Map not
to scale

285

to
Buena Vista

NATHROP

to
Salida

162   4.2 ml.

MT. PRINCETON
HOT SPRINGS

7.7 ml.

211

"Mt. Antero"

extremely rough
(see text)

MT. ANTERO

to
Mt. White

3.2 mi.

278

277

3.7 mi.

warning sign

to
St. Elmo

N

A variety of very nice mineral specimens have come from the renowned Calumet Iron Mine, northeast of Salida. Among the mine's most sought after minerals are sapphires, beautiful garnet crystals, delicate quartz crystals, and fantastic specimens of epidote, hematite, pyrite, green mica, diopside and feldspar.

To get to the old Calumet Mine, start at the corner of First and "I" Streets in Salida. Go north on Highway 291 toward Buena Vista exactly one mile and turn right onto County Road 153. Proceed two-tenths of a mile, crossing the bridge, and then turn right onto Spiral Drive. Follow Spiral Drive four-tenths of a mile as it turns northeast at the oil storage area. At that point, Spiral Drive goes right, but you should bear straight ahead on County Road 175 another six and six-tenths miles, then left onto County Road 185 another one and four-tenths miles. Turn right, still on County Road 185, passing a large quarry on the left, another one and three-tenths miles. The Calumet, Site A, will be seen on the hillside to the right. Follow the ruts to the dumps, approximately four-tenths of a mile farther.

Be advised that the ownership status of the Calumet Mine changes from time to time. At time of publication, a claim on the property was held by The Collectors Edge (303-278-9724) and access was restricted. Currently, collecting rights are only occasionally granted to groups with advance arrangements. If the property is still privately owned when you visit, simply continue to Site B.

If the Calumet is open or you have received permission to enter the property, park below and hike to the upper regions, looking for the thin schist layers. It is within that schist where many of the best sapphires have been found. Below the schist is a layer of marble, within which the garnets tend to occur. Sapphires generally are not gem quality, but, occasionally, crystals do have nice, clean, blue, facetable regions. Even if they are not gem quality, however, some are great for display in a mineral collection, especially if still attached to a portion of the host schist. The garnet is generally massive but sizeable single crystals can frequently be found by breaking up the marble.

The prize, green epidote crystals, regarded by many as among the finest to be found anywhere, are in cavities within softer portions of the limestone, generally near the contact region with the schist. In addition, lots of very colorful jasper can be picked up throughout the dumps, and some is filled with stringers, making it highly desirable for use in jewelry.

Marble, capable of taking a good polish, can be found by returning to County Road 185 and proceeding northeast about one-half mile farther to yet another mine, labeled Site B. Collectors at Site B can also find occasional beryl and garnet crystals, associated with quartz and mica.

CALUMET MINE

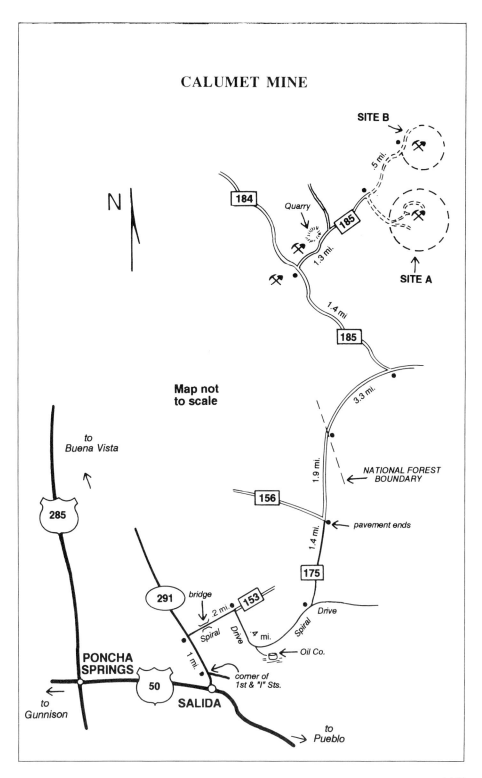

SITE B

184

Quarry

185

.5 mi.

1.3 mi.

SITE A

1.4 mi

185

N

Map not
to scale

3.3 mi.

to
Buena Vista

1.9 mi.

NATIONAL FOREST
BOUNDARY

285

156

pavement ends

1.4 mi.

175

291

bridge

.2 mi.

153

Drive

Spiral

.4 mi.

Drive

Spiral

Oil Co.

1 mi.

PONCHA
SPRINGS

50

corner of
1st & "I" Sts.

to
Gunnison

SALIDA

to
Pueblo

The three locations described here offer collectors a variety of minerals, including feldspar, mica, and garnet. To get to Site A, start at the corner of First and "I" Streets, in Salida. Go north on Highway 291 toward Buena Vista exactly one mile and turn right onto County Road 153. Proceed two-tenths of a mile, crossing the bridge, and then turn right onto Spiral Drive. Follow Spiral Drive four-tenths of a mile, as it turns northeast near the oil storage area. At that point, Spiral Drive goes right, but you should bear straight ahead on County Road 175 another six and three-tenths miles to where Road 181 intersects from the right.

Park near that intersection and climb to what remains of the abandoned quarry which is on the hillside directly opposite County Road 175. Since the mine is almost impossible to see from where you must park, just scramble up the hill until you encounter the overgrown access road and then follow it to the old workings. Site A boasts some very nice onyx-like aragonite as well as occasional specimens of actinolite and pyrite.

To get to Site B, continue along County Road 175 another three-tenths of a mile and turn left onto County Road 185 one and four-tenths miles farther. At that point, go left onto the faint tracks leading through a mine dump area to a gate, where you should park.

Hike along the old road a short distance to the main quarry, which is the center of Site B. Amongst the rubble, fine specimens of feldspar and mica can be found, as well as sometimes sizable beryl crystals and fascinating chunks of graphic granite. Pieces containing more than one mineral type, in association with each other, can be used as excellent display pieces in mineral collections. Don't hesitate to dig in the dumps or explore the surrounding countryside for more specimens.

Site C boasts nice garnet crystals, but access is not guaranteed, since it is necessary to cross through private property. If you would like to make an attempt, return to Highway 291 and proceed north toward Buena Vista two and seven-tenths miles. At that point, turn right, go one-tenth of a mile, crossing the railroad tracks, and then right again. From this road, the old garnet mine can be seen on the mountainside a few miles to the east. To gain access, inquire at any of the local ranch houses. Most of the farmers in this area are very accommodating, if given the courtesy of being asked before heading across their land. That is no guarantee, however.

If you do receive permission to proceed, head toward the mine one and seven-tenths miles on the sometimes rough dirt road. Once there, explore the dump area, splitting any suspect schist, in hopes of exposing garnet crystals. The crystals are often gem-quality and some are quite large. The schist tends to be somewhat green in color, and the best luck generally occurs in locations where it and the pegmatites come in contact.

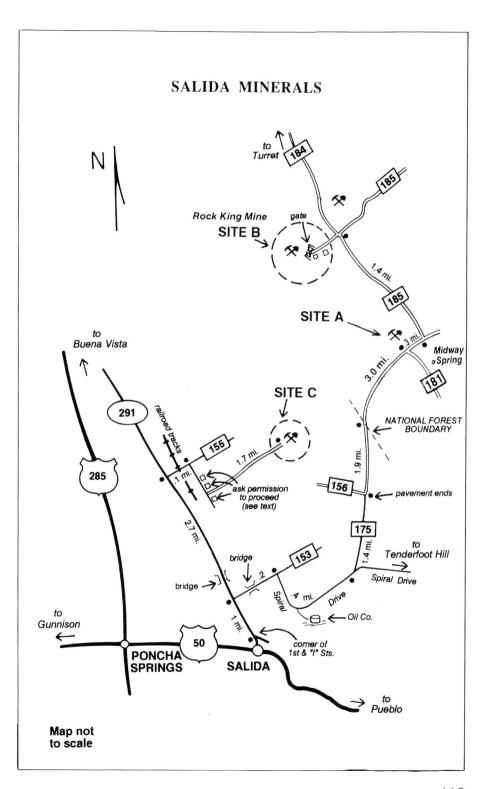

SALIDA MINERALS

N

to Turret

184

185

Rock King Mine
SITE B
gate

1.4 mi.

185

SITE A
.3 mi.

Midway
Spring

3.0 mi.

181

to
Buena Vista

291

SITE C

railroad tracks

155

1.7 mi.

NATIONAL FOREST
BOUNDARY

285

.1 mi.

ask permission
to proceed
(see text)

1.9 mi.

156

pavement ends

2.7 mi.

175

to
Tenderfoot Hill

bridge

153

1.4 mi.

Spiral Drive

bridge

.2

Spiral

.4 mi.

Drive

to
Gunnison

1 mi.

Oil Co.

corner of
1st & "I" Sts.

50

**PONCHA
SPRINGS**

SALIDA

to
Pueblo

**Map not
to scale**

The old Homestake Mine offers rockhounds a chance to find very nice pegmatite minerals and explore a massive and scenic quarry. Feldspar, mica and quartz, often associated with each other, can be procured within the dumps and throughout the surrounding countryside.

To get to this and one other interesting and photogenic site, start at the corner of First and "I" Streets, in Salida, go north one mile on Highway 291, and turn right onto County Road 153. Proceed two-tenths of a mile, crossing the bridge, and then go right onto Spiral Drive. Follow Spiral Drive four-tenths of a mile, as it turns northeast at the oil storage area. From there, bear straight ahead on County Road 175 another six and six-tenths miles and then left onto County Road 185 seven-tenths of a mile farther.

At that point, a very rough road goes up the hill to the right leading to the dumps marking Site A. It is strongly advised that you hike the approximate 400 yards to the old prospects rather than attempt driving, even if you have a rugged four-wheel drive unit. On and around the dumps one can find a milky-white common opal, but nothing especially noteworthy. Since you have come this far, however, the short side trip might be worthwhile.

Site B, the old Homestake Pegmatite Mine, is reached by continuing along County Road 185 another seven-tenths of a mile farther. At that point, the huge dumps can easily be seen directly ahead. Just before reaching them, County Road 185 turns right, and circumnavigates the huge quarry.

Park well off the main road and start exploring the mine and surrounding rubble. Be very cautious if you enter the old quarry, however, since the floor is flooded, and adjacent rock, if wet, can be quite slippery. So much can be found from within the dumps and amongst the debris at the base of the walls that it really isn't necessary to try removing specimens directly from the host rock.

As is the case with any mine, collecting status can change. If it appears that rockhounds are not allowed at either Site A or Site B when you visit, either restrict collecting to portions of the dumps adjacent to the road or explore some of the other nearby locations for similar pegmatite minerals.

*County Road 185
leading to the quarry*

HOMESTAKE PEGMATITES

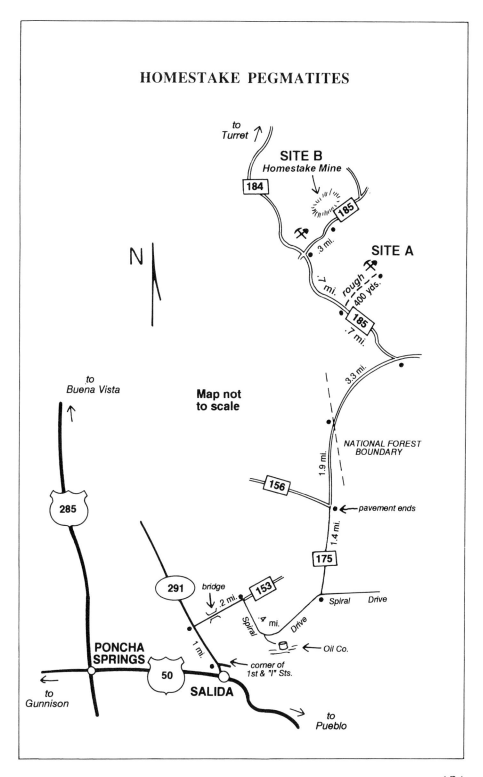

This location provides lots of fine minerals, including exceptionally well-formed feldspar, mica, lepidolite, tourmaline, beryl and even some topaz crystals.

To get there, start in the small town of Parlin, situated about eleven miles east of Gunnison on Highway 50. From town, go north on County Road 76 three and seven-tenths miles to where the road curves to the left. At that point, a graded dirt road intersects on the right, and it is there where you should turn. Immediately after leaving County Road 76, especially on the hills to the right, you will notice numerous prospect holes.

The area of primary interest, however, is reached by traveling east from the pavement seven-tenths of a mile and then turning right and following the ruts about half-way up the hill to the site of a small, abandoned mine. The ruts continue up to the ridge, but it is an extremely steep climb and not advisable or necessary.

Good specimens can be picked up all over the hills below the mine, and regions near the now sealed shaft are especially prolific. Acceptable specimens can usually be procured by breaking up the smaller rocks and boulders strewn among the rubble of the dump, making large scale excavations unnecessary.

Take time to roam the hillsides, carefully inspecting all suspicious outcrops and regions where previous prospectors have been working. These sites, although generally not as extensive, have been picked over considerably less than the mine area. Most collectors are satisfied with what can be obtained in and around the mine and do not venture much farther, thereby rewarding those who are willing to expend the extra effort.

Breaking down a boulder to expose other minerals

PARLIN PEGMATITES

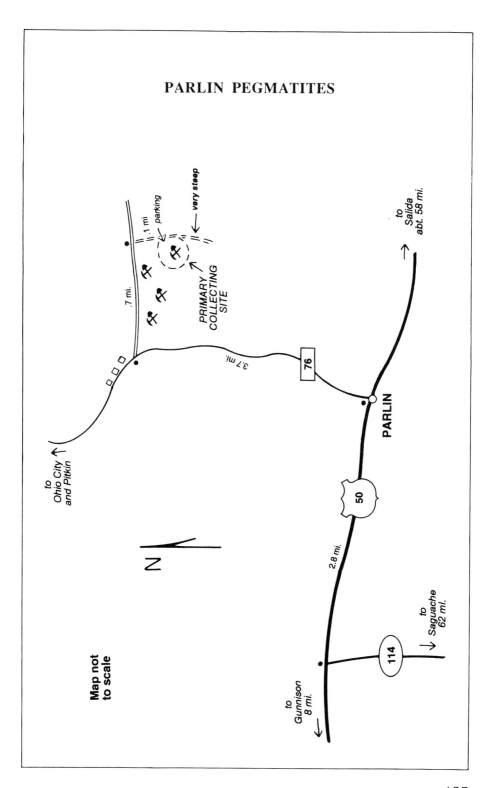

Map not to scale

N

to
Ohio City
and Pitkin ←

.7 mi.

.1 mi

parking

very steep

PRIMARY
COLLECTING
SITE

3.7 mi.

76

PARLIN

50

2.8 mi.

to
Salida
abt. 58 mi.

114

to
Saguache
62 mi.

to
Gunnison
8 mi.

Crystal-filled geodes, agate, jasper, opalite and chalcedony can be found in this well-known site which is nestled in the forested hills southwest of Saguache. To get there, take Highway 114 west from town fourteen and one-half miles to County Road 41G. At that point, turn south and continue six and three-tenths more miles to where there is a sign designating the turnoff to Lower South Fork. The turn is just before the road crosses over a metal drain pipe and the tracks will clearly be seen going up the hill on the west.

The best access to the primary collecting site is to park in the flat area just off County Road 41G, as illustrated on the accompanying map, and hike the old mine road or scramble up the hillside to the digging area. As you head toward the excavations, chips of agate and occasional pieces of jasper will be encountered, as will fragments of geodes, opalite and nice bubbly chalcedony.

It is suggested that you wait until you see what can be obtained at the main site before gathering much on the way up. Material seems to be more plentiful and of a higher quality in regions immediately in and below the primary diggings.

Since this spot is well known, most of the best surface material has already been picked up. Occasionally, however, the weather frees additional geodes and agates. If you want to find the best this location has to offer, it will be necessary to do some tough pick and shovel work in the rocky areas about half-way up the hill. The geodes primarily occur as large bubbles on the native rhyolite, and must be removed by chipping them away from the host rock.

This location is in a nice forested region, and the flat parking area affords a great place to set up a camp, if you choose to spend the night.

Walking the hillside for additional specimens

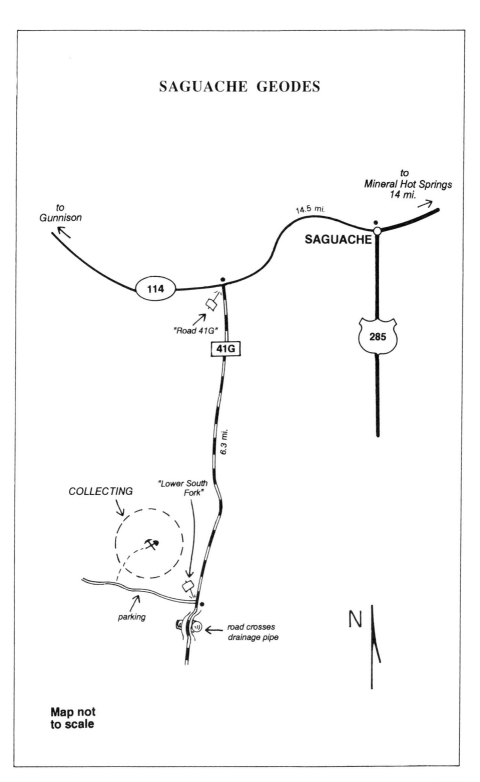

SAGUACHE GEODES

to Gunnison

to
Mineral Hot Springs
14 mi.

14.5 mi.

SAGUACHE

114

285

"Road 41G"

41G

6.3 mi.

COLLECTING

"Lower South
Fork"

parking

road crosses
drainage pipe

N

**Map not
to scale**

Delicate amethyst and clear quartz crystals can be obtained in and around the dumps of an old mine located in the hills northwest of La Garita. It is essential to mention that the mine was recently closed to rockhounds, due to the chemical leeching that had been done on portions of the dumps.

The site is only mentioned here in hopes that it will again be opened to collectors in the near future. DO NOT, under any circumstances, trespass onto the mine property if it is still posted. You may want to attempt gaining advance permission to visit by writing the current owners: Crystal Hill Mining Company, 13100 County Road 42-K, Del Norte, Colorado 81132.

Even if the mine is still closed, you might have some success searching portions of the dump immediately adjacent to the road or breaking up boulders in nearby washes and gullies in hopes of exposing crystal-bearing cavities. The trip is lengthy but what can be found could potentially make the trek worthwhile.

To get to the mine from La Garita, go north from town on County Road 42 two and two-tenths miles. At that point, turn left onto Road 42K and proceed six and four-tenths miles, bearing right at the two major forks, as shown on the map. Be advised that there are additional intersecting roads along the way, but, for all practical purposes, it is relatively simple to remain on the main thoroughfare. The mine is easily spotted as you approach, and there is a sign at the road leading to the dumps designating it to be "Crystal Hill."

The beautiful amethyst is found in veins and cavities throughout the host quartz rock, and those crystal-filled voids can be exposed by splitting any suspect stones in and around the dumps. This does involve some extremely hard work, and a good sledge hammer, strong gads and chisels, goggles, gloves and lots of energy are all essential. Look for boulders with exterior indications of "rotting." This is a good clue in regard to internal, crystal-bearing cavities and seams.

Some collectors have been able to find nice specimens by screening soil in the dump and nearby washes. If you obtain access to the dumps, digging and screening provides great potential for locating single crystals.

LA GARITA CRYSTALS

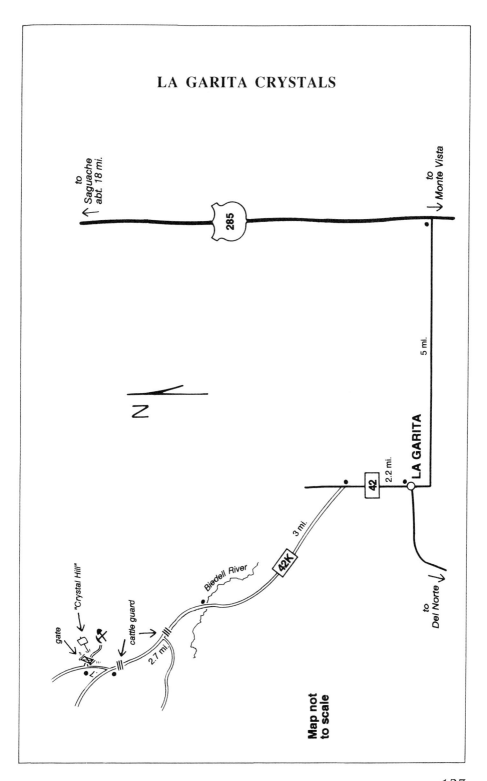

One of Colorado's premier locations for gathering glass-like Apache tears is situated in the foothills of Cochetopa Dome, a one-half hour's drive from Gunnison. The route to the collecting site, County Road NN14, is twenty miles south of Gunnison or forty-one miles north of Saguache, along Highway 114. If you spot a sign designating the route to Doyleville (County Road 14PP), you are one and three-tenths miles north of the turnoff.

Proceed southwest three and eight-tenths miles along County Road NN14 to where County Road KK14 intersects from the right. This is the northern boundary of the collecting area. A short distance beyond the intersection is a lengthy road cut filled with glassy Apache tears. Just about any portion of the terrain from there, continuing along County Road NN14 for at least another mile, affords great collecting potential, especially to the east.

The tears were formed as a result of the volcanic activity associated with the massive Cochetopa Dome and occur in much of the region's native rock. Specimens can be found on the ground or, in greater quality and quantity in any excavated region such as road cuts or areas of erosion. If you discover tears still partially embedded in the host rock, simply pluck them loose with the aid of a screwdriver or other similar tool.

County Road NN14 is well graded and, if dry, should not present a problem to most vehicles, if they are driven carefully. The Apache tears tend to be transparent and some even contain interesting inclusions which become visible after being tumble polished. Sizes range from quite small to occasional specimens measuring two or three inches in diameter.

Don't hesitate to do some walking in this geological interesting area. The best way to find Apache tears is to keep the sun to your back, thereby intensifying their color and contrast with the lighter colored soil.

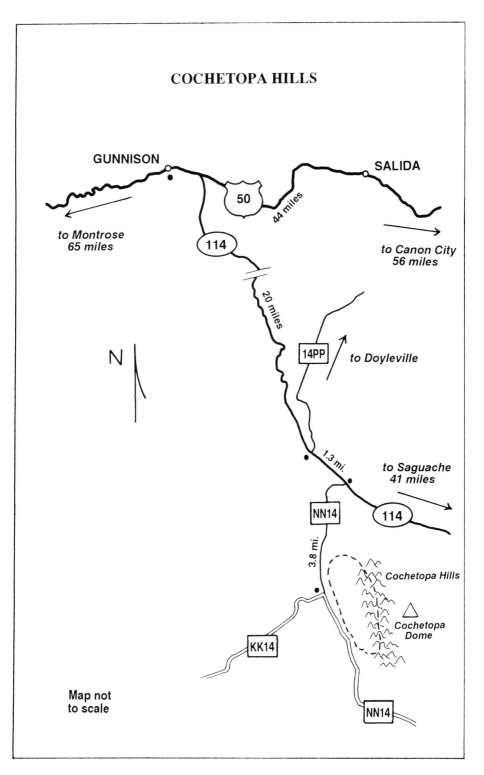

COCHETOPA HILLS

GUNNISON

SALIDA

to Montrose
65 miles

50

44 miles

to Canon City
56 miles

114

20 miles

N

14PP

to Doyleville

1.3 mi.

to Saguache
41 miles

NN14

114

3.8 mi.

Cochetopa Hills

Cochetopa
Dome

KK14

NN14

Map not
to scale

This is one of the most extensive agate fields in the entire state of Colorado, having provided rockhounds with tons of exquisite material over the years. To get to the center of this most productive deposit, go north from the town of Del Norte, on Highway 112, one-half mile. Just past the bridge, turn left toward the airport eight-tenths of a mile, and then left again, proceeding another two and eight-tenths miles. At that point, there is a fork in the road and virtually anywhere from there, continuing west and/or north for many miles, collectors have the opportunity to find agate and other minerals, generally in float scattered randomly throughout the terrain.

Two specific locations are illustrated on the map, but keep in mind that they are certainly not the only spots where you will have luck. This is one of those localities where days can be spent and the supply and variety is seemingly unending. Be advised that the roads can get very slippery if wet, and some of the auxiliary roads are very rough. For those reasons, four-wheel drive is highly recommended unless you only plan to search regions immediately adjacent to the main graded road.

Site A is accessed by going left at the fork and continuing two and four-tenths miles then turning north and proceeding one and six-tenths more miles. As you go, the road becomes rougher and rougher, so be sure to stop if you have any concerns about whether or not your vehicle can continue. At the given mileage, bear left, as the ruts parallel the wash.

Stop randomly along that wash and search just about anywhere to find lots of agate, with dimensions ranging from tiny pebbles to fist size. Much of the agate occurs in the form of tiny nodules and is fairly easy to spot due to its waxy appearance. This and Site B both boast beautiful plume, banded and dendritic agate, as well as unusually colored botryoidal chalcedony, dendritic opal, and even some interesting nodules, petrified wood and bloodstone.

Continue across the wash toward prominent Twin Peaks, which serve as landmarks for the center of this, the Del Norte Agate Field. You can spend hours and even days roaming the flatlands surrounding the peaks picking up an incredible variety of colorful and inclusion-filled cutting materials.

Site B can be reached by doubling back to County Road 66A, as shown on the map, heading north one and four-tenths miles, and then turning left onto well-graded County Road 660. Three and nine-tenths miles farther along, County Road 646 intersects, and that marks the start of Site B. Agate and other collectibles, as described earlier, can be found for quite a distance in just about any direction. Inspect the hillsides and drive along either of the two roads, stopping from time to time to gather what you desire from a seemingly unlimited amount of fine specimens.

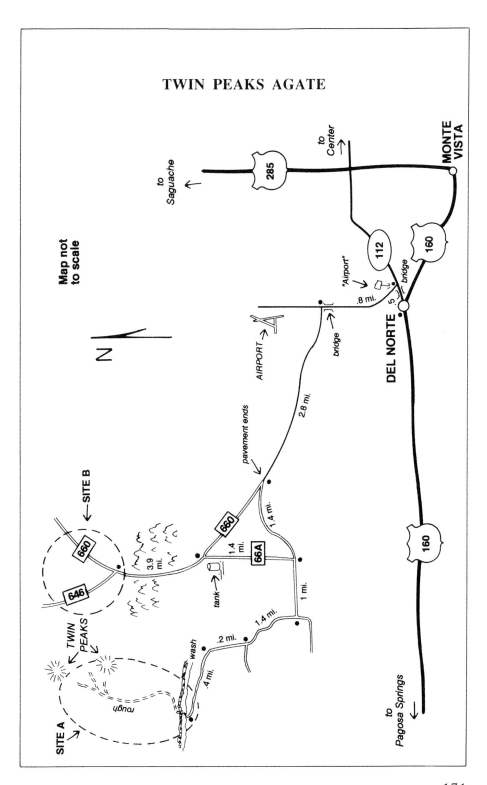

TWIN PEAKS AGATE

Map not to scale

N

to Saguache

285

to Center

MONTE VISTA

112

160

"Airport"

.8 mi.

bridge

.5

DEL NORTE

160

AIRPORT

bridge

pavement ends

2.8 mi.

SITE B

660

646

660

3.9 mi.

1.4 mi.

1.4 mi.

66A

tank

TWIN PEAKS

1 mi.

1.4 mi.

.2 mi.

wash

.4 mi.

rough

SITE A

to Pagosa Springs

This location is situated just off well-traveled Highway 160, and, for that reason, is not a place to take children or anyone else who has trouble moving fast. The highway bends around a blind curve a short distance away, and vehicles are not expecting to encounter someone on the pavement.

To get there from Pagosa Springs, go ten miles northeast on Highway 160 to where a road leads off to the right toward Treasure Falls. From there, continue exactly one-half mile along the steep and curved stretch of highway to the large road cut on the right. Be sure to pull completely off the highway onto the narrow turnout at the base of the road cut.

The geodes are found embedded within the native rock, either at the base of the road cut itself or on the other side of the highway, amongst the huge mass of rubble extending quite a distance down below. They are the result of a secondary filling of gas bubbles captured within the volcanic rock as it cooled.

The geode interiors are frequently filled with tiny, colorful quartz crystals, but, sometimes, other minerals are also present. Occasionally, the centers contain beautiful purple amethyst crystals, and, if such specimens are surrounded by solid banded agate, the result is a real prize. The amethyst isn't overly plentiful, however, and most is rather pale.

Be advised that every gas bubble does not contain crystals. Some are hollow or completely filled with agate, but, even in the latter case, the agate can be desirable, often being banded in shades of light blue and white.

The best method for collecting here is to first look for signs of agate or voids on the surfaces of freshly broken rock. Since the exterior of the geodes is virtually the same color as the host rock, they are extremely difficult to spot, otherwise. A rounded knob might be a clue. Since the agate is much harder than the host rock, it is not as susceptible to the forces of erosion, thereby maintaining its orbicular structure as the surrounding material is

eroded away. Chip off portions of suspect knobs or protrusions in hopes of either popping a geode free or exposing some of the whitish agate. This can involve lots of hammer and chisel work, not to mention patience, and some are much easier to remove than others, depending upon the host rock.

Collecting in the rain

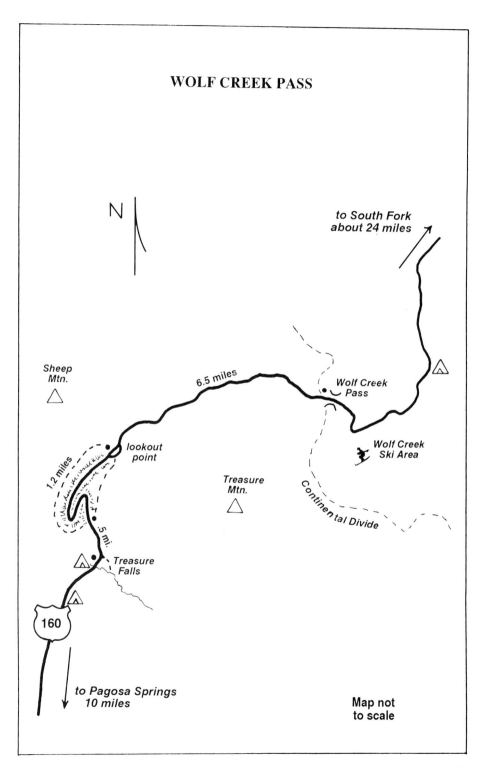

WOLF CREEK PASS

N

to South Fork
about 24 miles

Sheep
Mtn.

6.5 miles

Wolf Creek
Pass

Wolf Creek
Ski Area

lookout
point

1.2 miles

Treasure
Mtn.

Continental Divide

.5 mi.

Treasure
Falls

160

to Pagosa Springs
10 miles

Map not
to scale

The accompanying map illustrates some areas near Creede where fine mineral specimens have been found. Due to the nature of mining claims, however, no specific mine or dump is discussed. Instead, it is suggested that you restrict collecting to washes and ravines near the junction of West Willow Creek Canyon and East Willow Creek Canyon, as illustrated on the map.

If you do choose to inspect any of the many dumps in the region, it is essential that you do not trespass onto active claims. In addition, never enter the shafts, and always be on the lookout for rusty nails, broken glass, caustic chemicals or other hazardous materials.

If you cannot determine a specific mine's collecting status, try checking in town at a rock shop, or at the Chamber of Commerce. If you do not want to go to that trouble, a drive through this historically significant area is still fascinating and picturesque.

The list of minerals that have been found in the Creede mines is lengthy and includes amethyst, silver, sphalerite, galena, agate, chalcedony, quartz, pyrite, chalcopyrite, argentite, barite, chlorite, siderite, cerussite, malachite, chrysophase and fossils.

The fossil site is illustrated on the map and features primarily small insects and plants, embedded within layers of the native shale. The state of preservation is regarded as excellent, and portions of the host shale containing a number of fossils can be used to make outstanding display pieces.

If you have a four-wheel drive unit, consider taking the scenic drive to Wheeler Geologic Area. This is a fascinating and photogenic locality, worthy of the side trip, if you have the time and an appropriate vehicle.

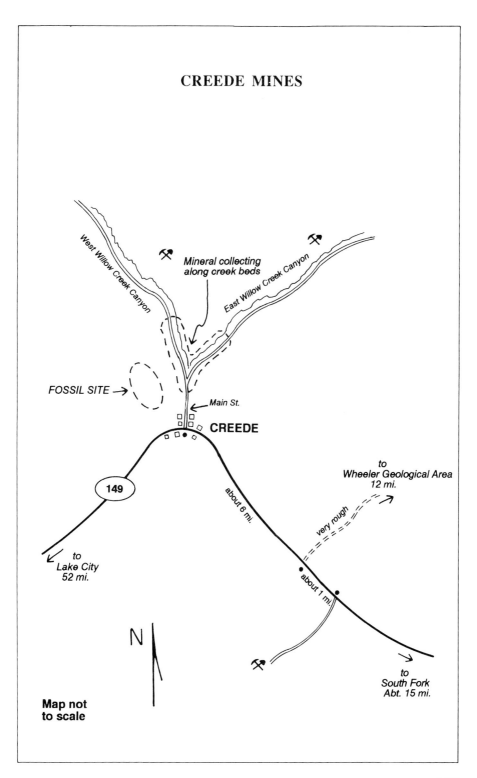

CREEDE MINES

West Willow Creek Canyon

East Willow Creek Canyon

Mineral collecting
along creek beds

FOSSIL SITE →

← Main St.

CREEDE

149

to
Wheeler Geological Area
12 mi.

about 6 mi.

very rough

to
Lake City
52 mi.

about 1 mi.

N

to
South Fork
Abt. 15 mi.

**Map not
to scale**

The accompanying map illustrates some of the major mines in the vicinity of Silverton. Due to the nature of mining claims, however, no specific mine or dump is discussed, since one that was open to collecting a week ago may be closed today, and vice-versa.

Be sure to remember, when exploring any of the mines in the Silverton region, that you do not trespass onto any active claims. In addition, never enter the shafts, and always be on the lookout for rusty nails, broken glass, caustic chemicals or other hazardous materials.

If you are unable to determine a specific mine's collecting status, check at a local rock shop, the Chamber of Commerce, or the County Recorder's Office. If you don't want to do that, a drive through this historically significant and extremely scenic area is still fascinating.

Many of the dumps extend down to the roadways where collectors can gather minerals, and erosion has carried additional specimens quite a distance from the mines into streambeds, washes and other low lying areas. Take time to explore those places and you might be well rewarded.

Minerals found in the Silverton area mines are numerous and include chalcopyrite, fluorite, galena, pyrite, quartz, rhodochrosite, gypsum, mica, sphalerite, barite, malachite, hematite, silver and gold.

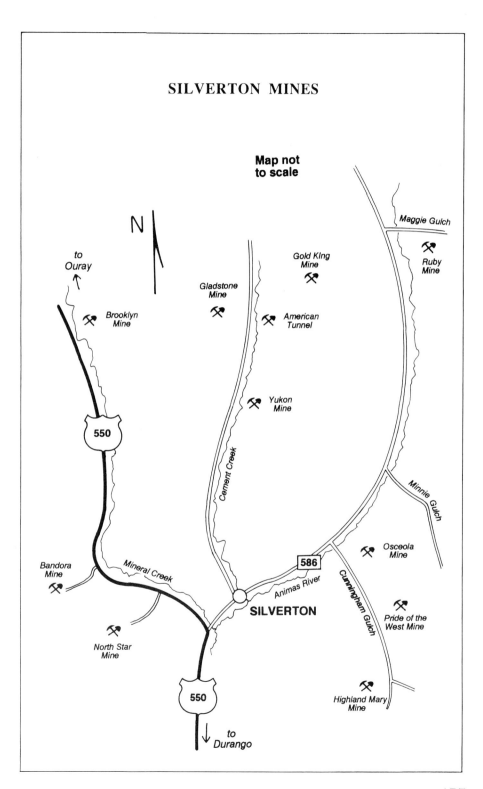

SILVERTON MINES

Map not to scale

N

to
Ouray

Brooklyn
Mine

Gladstone
Mine

Gold King
Mine

American
Tunnel

Maggie Gulch

Ruby
Mine

550

Yukon
Mine

Cement Creek

Minnie Gulch

Bandora
Mine

Mineral Creek

586

Osceola
Mine

Animas River

SILVERTON

Cunningham Gulch

Pride of the
West Mine

North Star
Mine

550

to
Durango

Highland Mary
Mine

One of the premier mineral localities in Colorado is the region in and around Ouray. The major specimen-producing prospects include the Camp Bird, Mountain Monarch, Silver Point, Grizzly Bear, Senorita, Bachelor, Longfellow, National Belle, Portland and Ohio Mines.

The list of what has been found in those mines is lengthy, with the most notable being nice crystals of chalcopyrite, fluorite, galena, pyrite, rhodochrosite, sphalerite, calcite, quartz, barite, azurite, and malachite. Many of the sites are still protected by a current claim, however, thereby being off limits to rockhounds.

Rather than create frustration by directing collectors to specific prospects in this still active mining region, the author has chosen to illustrate a few of the major mines and briefly discuss what type of minerals are available. Always get permission to collect on an active claim and never enter the mine shafts.

If you cannot determine collecting status, try checking in town either at a rock shop or the Chamber of Commerce. In any event, plan to take a drive through this historically significant area, since it is still fascinating and picturesque. The terrain surrounding Ouray is rugged and mountainous, though, so tough vehicles, preferably with four-wheel drive, are needed. Good and current road condition information should be obtainable in town, either at the Forest Service Office or at the Chamber of Commerce.

Many of the dumps extend down to the roadways where collectors can gather minerals, and erosion has carried some specimens from the mines into streambeds, washes and other low lying areas. Take time to explore those places and you may be well rewarded. If your vehicle can make the trip into the high country surrounding Ouray, be sure to make the journey, since it will allow you to see some of the most spectacular scenery in the state.

OURAY MINES

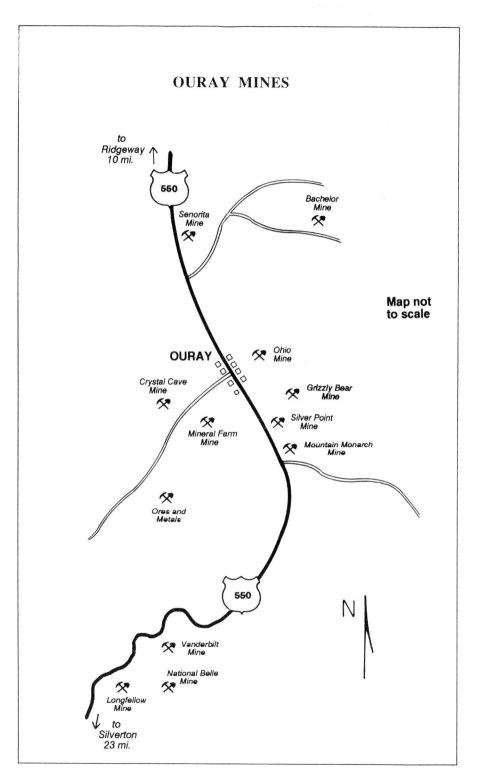

to
Ridgeway
10 mi.

550

Senorita
Mine

Bachelor
Mine

**Map not
to scale**

OURAY

Ohio
Mine

Crystal Cave
Mine

Grizzly Bear
Mine

Silver Point
Mine

Mineral Farm
Mine

Mountain Monarch
Mine

Ores and
Metals

550

N

Vanderbilt
Mine

National Belle
Mine

Longfellow
Mine

to
Silverton
23 mi.

MINERAL LOCATOR INDEX

MINERAL LOCATOR INDEX cont.